SO DISTANT
FROM MY LIFE

TRANSLATED BY

SO DISTANT FROM MY LIFE

MONIQUE ILBOUDO

YARRI KAMARA

TILTED AXIS PRESS

CHAPTER 1

When I awoke, timid rays of light had penetrated the room. My mind ran off as soon as I opened my eyes. I have always had a vagabond mind. That morning, it ran far, further than normal. It ran back in time, without my consent, leaping like a young goat released from its tether. Rather than fighting against this forced journey, I went along with it. For no reason, my thoughts stopped on that period when the obsession with emigration had taken over my life, my dreams, my desires, my very vision of the future.

My only desire then was to give myself a second chance. Leave. Go anywhere but here. Get far away from this life. Leave, live my dreams. Everybody has a right to that. What wrong had I done then? Our common quest is to try to live a better life. I sought to live better, a place to live better. Just a small corner on this vast earth where I, too, could blossom. To deter me, my uncle spoke to me about roots. A line of argument that I found absurd. Even plants are intelligent enough to grow around stones, seeking the best soil for their roots underground. My roots would grow wherever I found my happiness. That was my dream. Nothing more. *They* shattered it. I pieced it back together with what I could. Nothing is worse than resignation.

Yet, at the beginning, things had seemed off to a good start for a nice peaceful life where I was born. My parents didn't even have to stay up all night to secure a spot for me at school. Attending the white man's school had become the obvious choice for all; there were no longer other options. Like moths drawn to the neon lights of the growing city, our parents deserted the countryside in hordes. Once off the farm, the quest for new knowledge became a necessity. We definitely turned our focus on the science that unlocked doors to nice offices in Tangzugu, the hill where power was concentrated. Our parents dreamed of executive briefcases and diplomatic postings for their sons – for their daughters, it was still too early, that would come later. Everyone wanted to get in, but there were few schools and you had to get up very early to secure a place. Instead of spending a few sleepless hours tossing in their beds, parents would line up the night before registration opened and sleep under the starry sky of the school compound. A distant cousin, who was this little prince's caretaker, had thus slept in front of my future classroom to make sure that I would secure a spot. Our house was situated about a kilometre from the school. My cousin Nongma was one of the first in the interminable queue.

So, you see, I had not been dealt the worst hand at the beginning. I'll admit, I made some mistakes. Not in primary school where I was able to blend in with mediocrity. You know, the kind of pupil who is neither a whizz nor an outright dunce. The kind who slips through the cracks, forgotten. I passed my primary education certificate exams without much glory, certainly not well enough to open the doors to a public junior high school, where I could have continued my schooling free of charge. I messed up my entrance to junior high, the most unfair exam in the world, as I explained to my disappointed parents. My parents nonetheless decided to send me to one of the first private junior high schools that had just opened. The state had recently allowed entrepreneurs to invest in education, and schools sprung up like mushrooms. Were they to educate or to make profit? That was the question. And the answer, as is often the case, depended on the individual and how much faith they placed in humans or in capital.

My parents were not very rich. They registered me in an inexpensive school, the Lycée Privé de la Liberté, or LPL. For the uneducated founder of the lycée, the school was just another market in which to diversify his investments. The first friend I made at LPL was Manuel, may his soul rest in peace. Poor Manuel left us more than twenty years ago now. Like a lot of young people, Manuel thought death was an affair for the old. He was only seventeen at the time. Why would death steal from him his dazzling smile, his strapping form and the promise of long years to enjoy these things? The fateful day was the fifteenth of September. We were enjoying our last days of vacation before school opened again. Manuel had borrowed his cousin's brand-new scooter and come to see me. He wanted me to accompany him to Bonheurville, a new neighbourhood on the outskirts of the city. From the bawdy tone he took on when he told me he had to deal with something urgent, I understood that there was a girl involved. Manuel was already a formidable skirt-chaser, and I would take advantage of his leftovers. The prospect of meeting someone new, especially while on his cousin's hot new scooter, was tempting, and I accepted his request. At the last minute, however, I had a bad feeling and refused to get on behind Manuel for our planned expedition. I even tried to persuade him not to go, but he didn't listen and took off with a deafening roar of the bike's engine. I would only see his body again lifeless, flattened by a lorry, laid out on a stretcher when I rushed to the morgue as soon as I heard the terrible news. That was the day life turned its back on me. Or was it an amicable separation? In front of my friend's unrecognizable body, I understood just how precarious life was and I decided immediately to grab whatever I could from it. School, the air-conditioned office and all the rest were too long and too complicated.

I started hanging out with a bad crowd and slowly went off the rails. The first few times I ran off, my father moved heaven and earth to find me and march me back home. But he soon tired of this, and I lived on the streets for three years. Only the love and patience of my mother saved me from becoming completely lost.

One day, for at least the hundredth time, she stopped by the abandoned compound where we squatted, and found me still sleeping, groggy from the excesses of the previous evening. With a simple look, no tears or admonishment, she won over three years of futile rebellion. She took me by the hand and brought me back to the family nest. She handed me over to Association Bassawarga – literally, Association 'Has Left Misery' – who administered shock therapy. Between prayers for deliverance, corporal punishments and methadone, they managed to drag my head out of the muddy waters of street drugs within two months. I tried to pull myself back together. Going back to school, as my father insisted, quickly proved a complete fiasco. I was already twenty years old. The oldest in the year 10 class I returned to was just sixteen. I only stayed for a week. I tried vocational classes, apprenticeships, internships, but it was too late. You rarely recover from three years of rootlessness and assorted abuses. I could try all I wanted, but the snare around me was too tight. I made my dreams smaller. No more office with air conditioning or even a fan. I was ready to work hard under the burning sun, but nobody wanted the force of my young, vigorous negro arms. Nobody wanted to offer a reasonable price. The vigour of negro arms had been on sale for far too long. Discounted since the colonial days of forced labour, and even before then, since the days of slavery; never put back on the top shelf. Neither did anybody want the little know-how I had as a poorly educated African.

And so, I had to use trickery. And life doesn't like that. Generally, it tricks you right back, and harder. We had a tacit agreement. Life would open the world to me and I would pay in cash. Life is hardnosed in business. I paid a high price, very high.

CHAPTER 2

Shame doesn't kill. We would know if it did. And yet, they say he died of shame. When I opened my email yesterday I had at first jumped with joy. An email from Marité after such a long silence. She was the only link I had kept with my earlier life. My younger sister gave me her unconditional love. I knew that my leaving caused her great suffering, yet she never reproached me in the slightest, neither for leaving nor for my life choices. She was the one who gave me news from home every once in a while. On rare occasions, she let me exchange a few words with my mother. That only happened when my mother was able to escape the vigilant eye of her husband and visit Marité. The two conditions necessary for our brief conversations were then in place: an internet connection and distance from my father. For some weeks, I'd had no news from my sister, since she was travelling in remote regions not connected to the world-wide web. I jumped with joy when I saw her email with the subject 'News'. She should've written 'Bad News', as I understood from her first sentence: 'Papa is gone.' She lay out everything. The sudden death without any apparent cause. The unanimous diagnosis: 'Died from shame.'

My father was gone, and they say he died of shame. What did they know? Had they done an autopsy? Which organ did shame attack? The heart, the liver or the kidneys? My father was dead and I was not there to bury him.

My father and I had become strangers to each other. I had tried to talk to him, going through my mother, my sister or some compliant visitor whom I would call to pass the phone to my father without success. Toward the end, when news of my betrayal was confirmed, he uttered the ritual words of banishment. Until then, he had given me the benefit of the doubt. He had continued to go the neighbourhood savings and loans union to withdraw the money I sent by rapid transfer. I wasn't yet married, and he gave little weight to the gossip lashed by sharp tongues. 'Jealous people!' thundered my father in his stentorian voice when I called. 'My son, follow your path. I am telling you this. Your old man has faith in you. Let them braaay!!' he concluded, stretching out this last word in his inimitable fashion. I never had the courage to tell him he was wrong.

My father was the most open man in the world with his booming laugh, his kind air that put people at ease from the first contact. Sometimes he pretended to be angry, rolling his big eyes and serving us with specialities from the south of France, war souvenirs spiced with war-veteran French: *Patisangana! Partie sanglante* when a situation was particularly difficult, *Bougdandouille* for *Bougre d'andouille* to call someone a sausage bugger, or the ultimate insult *Estatue de Marseille-là*, indicating that the insulted was as frozen as a Marseilles statue!

But when my father closed up, nothing and nobody could soften him. Neither the furtive and contrite glances from my mother, ready to apologize for whatever she had committed or omitted, nor our sad or scared faces, which normally would've opened his protective arms.

My father was a war veteran. As a son of the village chief, he could have avoided conscription. Several chiefs had hidden their own sons and offered the colonists the progeny of their subjects as cannon fodder, some even sending cripples to meet the quotas demanded by the colonial administration. Perhaps my grandfather had been tempted to do this, but his two sons left him little choice in the matter. They were just kids, seventeen and fifteen, but they already had well-determined characters. Towering and formidable hunters, they couldn't imagine for one second remaining seated while the other young men of the village went off to war, even if it was someone else's war. They both signed up, to the great despair of my grandfather, who feared that his succession would be vacated for lack of a male descendant. Luckily, they came back from this war of '*Jamani*' and from the other fronts where they were sent for even less legitimate battles. My uncle was sent to Indochina and my father found himself in Algeria combatting former comrades who were now fighting for their independence. My uncle, the eldest, succeeded my grandfather a few years later. After a long while, my father, who had continued gallivanting around the world on his own, came back to his home country and settled in the city.

The two *tirailleurs*, who had left as Tanga and Tambi, came back with new names acquired on the baptismal fronts of Marseilles and Fréjus. Tanga, my uncle, chose the name Joanny, and my father Raphael. Tambi Raphael was almost forty years old when he came home. 'What a handsome man,' people would say of him. He was tall and svelte. True, the features of his face were not all regular: the wings of his nose were further forward than the tip, and the globes of his eyes protruded, but his fleshy lips had undeniable charm, particularly when they opened on his white and impeccably aligned teeth. Moreover, Raphael was always elegantly dressed and rarely took off his black Panama hat, which hid the beginning of a bald spot. Finding a spouse seemed to him the most sensible and the most urgent thing to do, and he undertook a methodical search for the lucky lady. He wanted a love marriage with a distinguished woman, and was satisfied beyond his expectations. A former regiment mate introduced Raphael to his cousin, who was the perfect candidate. Simone was twenty-five years old. She was born into a family that had converted to Catholicism very early on, which opened doors for her at the Catholic School of St Francis of Sales. While she did not study beyond fourth grade, this schooling bestowed her with a prestige that many women of her generation envied. She wasn't very tall but held herself nobly. Plus, she liked to wear heels and knew better than anyone else how to tie her silk headwraps high up, thus gaining a few precious centimetres. A first boyfriend had induced her to abandon school, only for the relationship to end. Simone then considered becoming a nun. She'd even started her noviciate, but was expelled when the convent's mother superior got wind of her aborted engagement from ill-intentioned gossips who also made insinuations about the novice's purity. Simone was forced to renounce her new vocation. Marité and I are eternally grateful for that. Such goes life, as Passektaalé the anonymous would say. Simone had just left the convent when she met Tambi Raphael. They married and settled in town, turning down an invitation from Joanny, who wished to have them close to him in the village. My father always said he'd made this choice for his Simone, who was 'born two inches from the city cathedral' and would not have managed the rigours of village life. It was clear that he wouldn't have relished a return to the countryside either. How could he have given up the daily 11:30 a.m. drink with his friends at Le Trou, the bar that served as their headquarters for reshaping the world, or his Saturday afternoon boules game, to mention just two activities that formed the rhythm of his life in the city. He was not sure that these city habits would have found a place in the village, and thus, the couple settled in the city.

We lived in Tangzugu, before the neighbourhood's inhabitants were evicted and resettled in the southern part of the city that was under construction. Despite Tangzugu meaning 'on the hill', you couldn't really call it a hill. Our city is so flat, and the colonizer found nothing other than this elevation on which to build the governor's palace. All around the palace, pretty houses, all of them painted white or in the local red stone, made up the European quarter, which became an administrative quarter after independence. The native Tangzugu quarter started beyond this prestigious circle and our house was on its limits. Rather unusually, our house, along with a dozen other houses, found itself in a sort of Bermuda triangle – not a dangerous one, but no less mysterious. The inhabitants of the triangle, my parents included, aspired to a social emancipation that wasn't always within their financial means. My father hadn't found a job both prestigious enough for his rank and unskilled enough for his lack of degrees. A blood prince who had *lived in France* could not be satisfied with a job as an office boy. Yet the only thing the public service offered him was to be an office minion whom everyone could call on to do this or that errand or to make one or the other delivery depending on their whims. My mother had to set up a tailoring shop in the front yard of the house. As her shop faced the prestigious side of the road, she sometimes had lady clients from high circles who crossed over to get adjustments made or dresses stitched for their little girls. My mother's tailoring business flourished for a while, and her income supplemented my father's pension, ensuring us a worry-free childhood.

Marité and I grew up in this relative affluence. We were always better dressed than our classmates at the Tangzugu school. This vestimentary prestige, which we had our mother's talent to thank for, was sometimes the source of unmerited envy. Some children would chase us to edge of the triangle, taking us for kids who had stumbled into this proletarian school from the fancy quarter. Later, Marité, who was a brilliant and studious pupil, moved on as a boarder at Our Lady of the Rosary Junior High, while I struggled on at my high school, Lycée Privé de la Liberté.

And then my parents' financial situation gradually took a turn for the worse. The rising cost of living in a developing city and my father's stagnating pension were one reason for this. In addition, my mother, who worked in the old-fashioned way, using sewing patterns, let herself fall behind the current styles and her patterns gradually become outdated. Her clients deserted her and she ended up closing shop. Thus, the family was just living on the quarterly pension, my father's *three months*. The battle for pension increases of indigenes hadn't yet been won, and what he received was barely enough for us to live on for the ninety days until the next payment. The last two weeks were always the toughest. We only saw our father early in the morning before he disappeared; he returned home late at night, once the household was asleep. My mother deployed a treasure trove of resourcefulness to meet our needs, starting with our dietary ones. To this day, I don't know how she did it, but Marité and I never slept with empty bellies. Finally, when the twenty-fifth of the month arrived, my father went out even earlier to be among the first at the French Treasury. On that day, he would return around 1:00 p.m., lighthearted, arms filled with presents. Two months of financial stability would follow, until the third.

CHAPTER 3

Cities are like human beings, you should never trust appearances. Some cities are beautiful but hard; others are less classy but soft and welcoming. Dignity is not shared equally among cities. Some cities are ready to bare themselves to the first tourist that comes along, to reveal all to any visitor who pokes their nose around the corner.

Ouabany belonged to this latter category. The city offered itself from the very first glance, not out of vice but out of simplicity and generosity. Brazen visitors didn't hold back. They assaulted the city with no inhibition, subjecting it to their antics. Us young natives of Ouabany were a little outraged by how loose our city was. We would have liked her to be more mysterious, more prudish. Out of jealousy, we would play tricks on tourists, just for fun or sometimes to swindle a few notes from them. The trick was a simple one: complicate a route that was not complicated and get paid to guide the tourist. This worked best when we operated in pairs. The second fellow would arrive to rescue the poor tourist, chastising the first for having needlessly complicated the route, and would take over to guide the unlucky visitor to their destination, getting rewarded even more generously. During my three years of vagrancy, I often played this trick with my partners in crime.

That is why I immediately recognized what was going on when one day, around noon, I came across two youths pretending to fight, one accusing the other of having lied to his friend and proposing they backtrack and find the right way to the Mining Permits office. There was no real administrative district in Ouabany. A few buildings near the State House lodged the prime minister's office and a few other ministries, while most of the other administrative offices were spread out across the city, housed in buildings rented from private owners. I stopped for a little bit of entertainment. The office in question was situated on a road parallel to the one where we stood. One of the youths suggested that the gentleman accompany him to the closest taxi stop, as the Mining Permits office was across town. The gentleman, a white man, was dressed in a wrinkled blue linen jacket, oversized trousers and shabby sandals. The other young fellow insisted that the office was only ten minutes away on foot, and offered to accompany *his friend* there. The gentleman, unperturbed, turned toward me. I thought he was going to ask for my advice, but he didn't. He just looked at me insistently. The man's gaze reminded me of the way I took in the anatomy of pretty girls. I didn't like it. On top of his indecent gaze, his dirty and scruffy look made me detest him. To punish him, I was about to give a hand to the two guys, when, leaving all three of us, he walked off a few steps, took out a mobile phone and called someone who must have been his driver.

'Rasmané, are you free? Can you come please? Just on the corner where you dropped me.' And then, seeing the shade of a flame tree in front of a compound, he said to us with a malicious smile: 'Come my friends. We can continue the discussion while waiting for my car.'

The youths, thrown off their game, moved off in search of easier prey. I also wanted to continue on my way.

'You are not by chance looking for a job?' asked the man.

As calmly as my heart, that was leaping like a goat, allowed me, I joined him under the flame tree. I detested him, but I detested the poverty I eked out a living in even more.

Following my refusal to return to the school benches and my unsuccessful attempts at finding any kind of training, my father had tried to kick me out of the house, but my mother had persuaded him not to. She had gone to great lengths to pull me back into the family fold, and had no intention of letting the reins go so soon. She nonetheless suggested that I find employment quickly. My father would start his offensive again if he saw me mulling around all day doing nothing. With my back to the wall, I assessed what inexistent skills I had. It was while drafting a letter for my cousin Nongma that the idea came to set myself up as a public letter writer. I had always liked writing letters, especially for others. When Manuel was around, it was I who drafted notes to soften the hearts of girls, before Manuel, with his gift of the gab, provided the finishing touches. I convinced my mother to loan me money to buy a table, a chair and a bench; and I set up shop under the shade of Doulaye's food stall on Avenue 58.

Everything went well the first few months. A carpenter friend had made a nice signboard for me: Business letters – Beautiful love letters – Debt recovery letters – All your letters – Cheap prices. I didn't like the last line, 'Cheap prices', which he had added as a favour to me, but I didn't say anything. Anything free comes with a price. My lovely signboard brought in my first customers, who, satisfied, brought in more customers. Within a few months, my bench was never empty and

Doulaye, the shopkeeper, thanked me for the customers who sometimes passed me and went and sat on his high stools to order a coffee or tea or even an omelette or fried eggs while awaiting their turn.

I had not done any market study and simply hoped that by setting up shop I would have an occupation to get me out of the house each morning and back home in the evening like a 'real worker', thus avoiding my father's wrath. Something for the time being. I was as surprised as any other by the success of my business.

Business went so well that after a year I was able to deposit some money in the local savings and loans union. I bought a dictionary from a street vendor nearby and spent my spare time looking up words. My vocabulary became increasingly varied and specialized.

I brought home a bag of rice each month and this filled my mother with pride. My father was no longer consumed by the simmering anger that had made him grumble like the end of a storm, eyes filled with sparks, ready to explode each time our paths crossed. As for Marité, who was preparing for her A-level exams, being able to slip her a banknote every now and then made me her hero. I didn't intend to write letters my whole life. I had greater ambitions. But for the time being, I was enjoying this peace. It lasted a little more than three years.

And then, one day, I saw two young ladies arrive. Not for an instant did I think that their arrival signalled the end of my hustle. To be honest, I did greet them with some hostility. I had nothing but contempt for these outlandish girls with their orange skin stained with dark blemishes, vestiges of their original skin colour. They irritated me to the extreme. These ladies were not only peeling off their skin, but they also wore outrageous make-up and were perched on stilts that made their bottoms, squeezed into too-tight jeans, waddle.

'We have new neighbours. They've taken over the *diaspo* place,' Doulaye explained to me.

He appeared in awe of the two intruders. He crossed the road to talk to them. 'They are opening a cyber!' specified my *hoster*. Yes, I know that word does not exist. I searched for it in vain in my dictionary. Those whom we called 'diaspos' were a group of young people whose accent gave away their birth in a neighbouring coastal country. We never knew how many of them there had been. Their numbers varied from month to month. Only Sam and Paré were permanent. When I had first set up shop on Avenue 58, their hair salon, the New Style, was always busy. Their boom box was so powerful that for more than fifty metres, the whole street could dance to the latest hits they played, and some did just that. Doulaye's food stall was adjacent to the wall of his uncle Mr Nakamba's house. Only Mr Nakamba complained about the ruckus, without success. Then Sam, 'the king of the clippers' and manager of the salon, had returned to the coast of his birth. And the New Style slowly went downhill.

After two weeks of renovations, the new neighbours put up a sign that announced: Chez Fatou and Malika: Secretarial Services – Cybercafé – Hair pieces and jewellery on sale. While putting away my work tools that evening, a question insidiously entered my mind: what did they mean by secretarial services? The next day, like a harbinger of my downfall, my bench remained empty. Just one old ma came in the late afternoon, holding an envelope that was still closed. She wanted me to read her a letter from her son who had left five years ago for America. 'It's my nephew who normally reads his letters and writes back for me. But I don't think he really writes what I tell him to. Why can't my son come and visit if he is working there? He sends me more money than I need, but what I really want is to see him again!' I opened the letter and read it to the old lady, who did not seem pleased. 'It's always the same answer. What is this green card business?' she asked me. I tried to explain, as well as I could, the situation her son was in. He had written saying that crossing the borders of his host country before he obtained his resident card, the infamous green card, meant it would be impossible for him to return there. After the dismayed old ma left, I decided to cross the street. I had to go and see the den of those two lady tigers. When I entered, the room seemed larger than it had been when it was still the New Style. On the right were three chairs stuck side by side, on which three customers sat waiting. Two other customers were pounding away on the keyboards of two computers that were connected to the internet. A softwood desk stood in the back of the room. Malika, behind a third computer, was talking with a customer seated in front of her. On the left, near the entrance, stood a majestic shelf with a glass display full of shiny imitation jewellery. On the ceiling, two fans nonchalantly spun their brand-new blades.

'Welcome neighbour!' cried Fatou, closing the window of the jewellery display. 'How kind of you to come and see us,' she continued, holding out her hand to me – it was fine-skinned, streaked with blue veins, and had darkened joints.

That was the only time I got close to those devils who had come to steal the bread out of my mouth. The success of their cybercafé, one of the first in the city, inspired other entrepreneurs. We were entering the third millennium and young people here and elsewhere could talk of nothing else but 'internet', 'connection', 'email' … I could have survived with the elderly who made up the stock of my customers. However, another event precipitated my decline: the mobile phone made an even more dramatic entry into the local market.

Marité, who was doing a master's in development economics, explained to me that the government had just liberalized the telecoms industry and two private mobile phone operators, who had been waiting impatiently, had set up operations. Their headquarters were in buildings that faced each other on the market street. Competition had led to a fall in prices, making the mobile phone more affordable and democratized. My sister, whose thesis was on the impact of new information and communications technologies (she called them NICTs) on development, would not shut up about the issue.

'On the radio, they're talking about the "digital divide", but for me, seeing how everyone, young and old, man and woman, is going crazy, I feel that what we have coming is a revolution,' she added, happy to have an attentive ear within the family circle.

I have to say, she was not wrong. Today we talk of the 'technological leap' Africa accomplished passing from fixed phone lines to mobile phones. At the time though, I didn't care much for these economic considerations, I was only concerned with my *bizness* being in danger. Within two months, the two developments had put an end to my career as a public letter writer. I didn't change anything about my habits for a few months. I resorted to emptying the account I had opened at the savings union to meet my expenses. When all that remained was the minimum deposit required to keep the account open, I sold the table, chairs and bench, which a sympathetic Mr Nakamba had allowed me to keep in a corner of his com-

pound. At home, only Marité knew that my career had been
cut short. She helped me as best she could, taking money from
her meagre student scholarship to bail me out. *Truth cannot be
hidden for long*, says the African adage. After two months passed
without a bag of rice being delivered to our house by donkey
cart and not a bottle of *Kiravi* placed on the sitting room table
for my father, the secret came out by itself.

I endured the return of my father's end-of-storm grum-
bling, head lowered, but my mother's anguish, her sighs and
looks of despair, were harder to take. Still, this all seemed less
frightening to me than the streets. The virtuous life makes you
soft. During the time when I *delinquented* – yes, I know it is a
neologism. I have a dictionary: you have *delinquent* the noun
and the adjective, and then comes *deliquesce*. How much do
you *delinquent* before liquefying? I had tested those dangerous
waters. In those days, we avoided some neighbourhoods,
where stones were too quick to be thrown. We knew that
while a motorbike stolen in the posh Résidence du Bois would
lead you to the police station, the slightest thievery in Karpala
got you a one-way ticket to hell. One of our mates from the
squat, Tibo, had downplayed this danger. No doubt tempted
by the prospect of easy gain, one day he tried to pinch a cloth
money holder that women usually wear around their waists.
The second-hand goods seller, very busy that day, had left hers
lying around, filled with crumpled banknotes, under the corner
of the black plastic carpet on which she displayed her wares:
old stuffed toys next to second-hand underwear and rusty cut-
lery. 'Goodbye Europe' items that people jostled each other to
examine, to touch, to buy. Somehow Tibo, though not a
novice, let himself be tempted. He managed to furtively pick
up the small lime-green velvet bag and keep it hidden with the

green of a stuffed duck he had bought. The seller didn't see anything, but the suspicious gaze of one of the clients caught her attention. Instead of handing Tibo a plastic bag to put his purchase in, she asked for the stuffed duck to put it in the bag herself. Tibo insisted on taking the bag and, from there, things fell apart. The client pulled the string of the green bag, and the seller, glimpsing her treasure, cried out: 'Thief! Thief!' That was all that was needed. In less than twenty-five minutes, Tibo was nothing more than a mass of bleeding flesh in the middle of the pile of rocks and brick debris that had been used to stone him. The news quickly made the rounds on the street and we went with our other partners in crime to watch the macabre show at the eastern entrance of the Karpala market. A mother, taking pity, ended up covering the corpse of poor Tibo with a wrapper. The police finally arrived after several hours. A few superficial questions followed, and then the body was taken to be buried by prisoners in a nearby cemetery. That incident marked me deeply. It was soon after that that my mother came to take me back home. I knew that the situation, despite all the campaigns against mob justice, far from getting better, had got worse. I no longer had the insouciance of a sixteen-year-old and didn't want to live with such dangers. I dug myself into the security of the family nest, while looking for an escape route.

That was my situation when that white man, with his dirty and scruffy look, threw at me the question: 'You are not by chance looking for a job?' Do you ask a blind person if they want their sight back?

Rasmané had returned, not in a shiny luxury car, but in a rattletrap, one of those banged-up green taxis. It was an antique outdated Toyota that swayed on the road like an old drunk.

The white guy invited me to climb in the back and he got in the front. After a stop at the Mining Permits office, where the white man quickly dropped off his file, Rasmané drove us along Myriam Makeba Avenue, one of the town's liveliest streets. I followed my future employer to the third floor, with no lift, still mute, eyes brimming with hope. Even when he opened the door of the apartment and I saw the mess and filth, I followed him. I was ready to clean up this pigsty to get the money to pay an agent if that's what it took. I was ready to do just about anything to get away from my misery. Just about anything, but not what he tried as soon as the door shut behind us. I thank the stars that there was nothing more dangerous at hand. Otherwise, I would be rotting behind bars right now. The colonial statue that I picked up was a metre long, but it was sculpted in lightweight wood. I hit him as hard as I could and leapt for the door.

CHAPTER 4

My uncle, the chief, told me an incredible story one day. If you lay down a chicken and place a knife on its neck saying to it, for example, 'Don't move, I'm going to the market and when I come back I'm going to slit your throat,' the chicken will not move until you come back from the market and kill it. Try it, you'll see.

I wasn't a chicken. I refused to remain lying down where chance had birthed me. I refused to be a collateral victim of International Monetary Fund structural adjustment programmes. I refused to silently suffer the carelessness of those in charge. I grabbed my destiny by its horns. I looked it straight in the eyes and gave orders. Come what may! My plan was simple: One, get out of this rathole as soon as possible. Two, go and make a fortune in Europe, or even better, in the land of Uncle Sam. Three, come back and live like a king, taunting all those who treated me like dirt.

From here, the grass looked very much greener in the pastures of the neighbouring continent. Lambana claimed to have seen them. He also said that the European coastline was closer to Africa than people said. Lambana was a former classmate, but he had paid more attention to the teacher, as my mother says. He became a police officer. He had just returned from a six-month training course in Algiers, cloaked in new-found prestige. The fact that he had succeeded in joining the police corps had already set him apart from the rest of us, the future-less ones. But that he had got so close to those coveted coasts and had come back 'to serve', as he asserted with a certain emphasis, elicited the admiration of all the mothers in our neighbourhood. 'Only God knows why,' sighed some mothers rather cryptically.

In the stories of his mythical trip, Lambana compared the Mediterranean to the dam that separated our neighbourhood from the one on the opposite bank. He claimed that from Algiers you could see the town of Marseille and the green pastures that surrounded it. We all knew that Lambana was a serial exaggerator, but we wanted so badly to believe him! We wanted so badly for those coasts to be closer, more accessible. Virtually, they had come much closer in recent times. Thanks to satellite we could now, in real time, watch the same programmes on television as the lucky inhabitants of the countries where good and beautiful things were available to all. Though not at our house where we only had an old TV − colour, but so capricious that every now and then you had to slap it to get it to work. We received the sole national TV channel, but in some of the better-off homes, satellite dishes on rooftops signalled subscription to a package of a dozen channels. The less well-off among us could watch some of these channels at Modou's. Modou was the neighbourhood basket case. Mothers said his name only to express pity for his mother or to feel better about their own offspring. 'That poor woman,' you would hear, 'suffering nine months for that! If at least she had had another child,' or 'Mine at least got his primary certificate or his junior high certificate,' or 'Mine at least is a mechanic, a welder or an electrician ...' Hajja Safiatou was a gentle and modest woman. She watched over her only son like a mother hen and put an abrupt end to any discussion if she sensed the slightest criticism of him. At almost thirty years of age, Modou had never made the least attempt at emancipation. Some claimed that he still slept in the corridor outside his mother's room, refusing even to move into one of the rooms in the bachelor wing that had been built on one side of the family's large compound to house their young men.

Then satellite TV came and Modou found his calling. He convinced his father to subscribe to the basic package and free up the vestibule at the front of their compound where the old man spent his days and received his visitors. Old El Hajj, as he was known in the neighbourhood, had been a successful trader. When he'd returned from his pilgrimage to Mecca, he gave up his spot in the Ouabany central market to his son Issa, Modou's half-brother. From then on, he spent his days reading the Qur'an, reciting verses and fingering his prayer beads, only interrupting this ritual to receive visitors or go for prayers at the nearby mosque. Another entry had to be built on the western side of the compound wall, in front of the enormous beechwood tree under which the old man now sat. In the re-arranged vestibule, Modou set up benches, opened his cinema and welcomed us in exchange for a fee. Twenty-five francs each time we stepped through the outer door. I preferred the real cinema downtown. However, some evenings it was easier to get a hundred-franc coin from Marité or my mother than a five-hundred-franc bill. You needed a hundred francs to really spend a good evening at the vestibule, twenty-five for entry and twenty-five for each of the three glasses of tea that Modou would prepare while watching us out of the corner of his eye.

During the hot season, he set up his small brazier outside and brought us the three tea servings on a tray. When the Harmattan winds blew and the nights grew cool, he brought the stove indoors and it heated up the room.

We tried to negotiate a daily rate, but Modou refused to budge an inch on the price. And so we stayed as long as we could to get the most out of our francs. Nevertheless, at some point one always had to step out for an errand, to eat or to respond to a call from a friend or relative asking for help. Despite the draconian measures imposed by the master of the place, several of us were regulars at this neighbourhood cinema. The vestibule was often full to the brim, especially on football match days. We were as fascinated by the adverts as we were by the matches. Faced with the orgy of luxury, of shops, of windows and shelves overflowing with all types of products, we could do nothing but dream of getting close to such paradise on earth. One particularly boring evening, I found myself at Modou's. There was no match on, but I was ready to watch any film while waiting for everyone at home to go to bed. When I arrived, Modou took my twenty-five-franc coin, the second of the day, closed the door and then went through the interior door toward the compound. Someone had called his name from inside. I sat down as a commercial break was ending. A documentary started. We hated documentaries. This one was called *Stop Food Waste*.

The three guys who were already there shouted in unison, 'Modou, change the channel!' In order to remain the master of programming and avoid fights between clients, Modou never let anyone else touch the remote control. He came back, asked us which channel we wanted, but our ravenous eyes were now riveted on the screen. Tons of meat, milk, eggs and other food products were being thrown in pits to be destroyed. The opening scenes of the documentary had left us speechless. In unison, we signalled *It's okay!* and Modou went back inside the compound. For half an hour we witnessed, in shock and silence, monstrous waste. One of the other three spectators found the force to say out loud, 'Why? Can't they send that stuff to us?'

The next morning, when I told my sister about the documentary, she retorted in a mocking tone, 'It's the law of the market!' That very day, I made the decision to migrate.

My first attempt to reach the banks of the prosperous West was nipped in the bud by the hungry pockets of my agent. I had been saving with him for several months, when one day he vanished into thin air without a word (we would have trounced him had we known), taking my savings with him. Yet Raso had been well known among aspiring migrants. Ten or so guys had successfully migrated thanks to him. This had gained him a solid reputation, which had attracted another dozen candidates for economic exile.

Once one started depositing their savings, they could not turn back. Giving up on the journey then meant losing hard-earned, or sometimes borrowed, cash. Investigations found that while Raso may not have completed his first year of economics at university, he'd had time to learn some tricks. 'It's the classic scam,' Marité explained to me. 'He respected the contract with his first customers to gain people's trust and attract new customers.' And it had worked. He patiently amassed a neat pile of cash before disappearing. Where to? No one was able to find out.

I had to start from scratch again – doing the rounds of paternal and maternal uncles, some trader aunts and even some friends who already had jobs. During my first attempt, some of the relatives I asked for help had tried to dissuade me from going ahead with an endeavour they judged perilous. My uncle, the chief, had tried to appeal to my sense of patriotism: 'Your father and I, we could have stayed in France, but we came back because this is where our roots are. And who is going to build our country, if you, the youth, leave?' My mother, for her part, cried: 'Wooii! My dear son, don't do this! It's too dangerous. Do you not watch TV? Do you not see what is happening? The great sea is insatiable! She swallows all those who try to cross her and spits them out lifeless!' I had great difficulty persuading her. In the end, the example of a neighbour's son who managed to make it to the other side convinced her. She handed me her meagre savings, which that bastard Raso had stolen along with the rest. I never found the courage to tell her. I started saving with another agent, pretending I hadn't yet finished with the first.

More than a year later, I finally set off. With their eyes reddened by tears, my mother and sister said their wrenching goodbyes to me under a moonless sky. My father hadn't been informed of my plans. This second attempt got me a little bit further, but still not to my intended destination. Having left Ouabany in the middle of the night, I got to Agadez five days later. The journey to Tamanrasset was the most trying. Packed in the back of a truck transporting sand, we had to take turns sitting. We drove mostly at night. During the day, most of my fellow travellers danced barefoot on the platform made scorching hot by the burning sun. Some ended up taking off their clothes to wrap them around their feet. I was one of the few privileged ones, I had second-hand sneakers that more or less protected the soles of my feet. Between flat tyres and various breakdowns, we reached Tamanrasset after a three-day ordeal. According to my calculations, this leg of the journey should have lasted just a few days, but I ended up staying weeks in the small Saharan town.

I met Henri in Alouette where I had followed two other travellers more experienced than me. Alouette was where one went when you got off your truck. All migrants passing through Tamanrasset stopped by at one point or another during the day. It was here that you could get the latest news and learn from the experiences of others. Henri's black T-shirt with MC Solaar scrawled on it grabbed my attention. I was a fan, and had the same T-shirt. Henri had taken off from Yaoundé in Cameroon. Robbed during the journey, he had been trying for two years now to rebuild his nest egg, taking on jobs as a porter – he who had quit a job as a nurse to 'seek adventure'. In Henri's mouth, 'seek adventure' took on another sense, and while danger wasn't excluded, he left no space for chance. Like me, my new friend was sure of himself. Just a few towns, a desert and water to cross, and then success and money awaited us, quietly, on the other side. This wasn't the only thing we had in common. Henri didn't wear MC Solaar on his chest for nothing. Like me, he loved words, and we spent hours reading the dictionary I had brought with me, discussing the meanings of words, learning new things. We stayed together until Oujda. Unfortunately, a few weeks after our arrival, Henri was caught up in a massive round-up of hundreds of migrants. They were expelled. We later learned that they numbered more than five hundred. They were deported and abandoned in the desert between Algeria and Mali. I tried to spot Henri among the few survivors who were later found. A French TV station broadcast the images. Their faces – burnt, emaciated and unrecognizable – evoked the inmates of Auschwitz. To this day, I hang on to the idea that he might have survived and I just did not recognize him in the images.

I lived for a year and a half in Oujda. Did I really live? I survived, I got by, exhausting my meagre resources and accepting the worst menial jobs to earn my daily bread.

Several times I took part in attacks from the town of Nador without any success. What we called an 'attack' consisted of several dozens of us hurling ourselves against the barriers on the Ceuta and Melilla borders. Twice or thrice I reached the second row of barbed wire, the highest and the sharpest. My wounded hands and feet forced me to turn back to the camp to treat them. And then there came the round-up, which temporarily put an end to my hopes of conquering the damned iron wall to finally live my dream. After getting seriously injured during yet another attack, I joined some compatriots in the Sidi Maafa Forest to recover in peace. That's when the Moroccan police decided to go migrant hunting. Unable to run due to my injuries, I could not get away from them and was arrested. Just before getting injured, I had helped Monsieur Ben Yahia and his family move house. They were leaving Oujda to move to Meknès. I accompanied them to their new house and Monsieur Ben Yahia issued a sort of payslip for me so that I would not get hassled on my way back. He was a classy guy, who moreover had paid me well, unlike most others who exploited our precarious situation. Some even refused to pay us once we finished our work, and threatened to call the police if we insisted. Monsieur Ben Yahia's kindness betrayed me. An inexperienced diplomat at our embassy in Rabat confirmed to the Moroccan authorities that, given my name, I was certainly one of their nationals. I was repatriated on a direct flight with Royal Air Maroc. My first trip on a plane.

I had communicated very little with my family since my departure two years ago. My father did not scold me. Rather, he was relieved to see me, as the number of migrant boats sinking had increased in the past months. My mother and Marité danced with joy before they saw the gashes on the soles of my feet. The wounds had started getting infected and I was only able to stand through superhuman effort. I spent a month in hospital. When I was back on my feet, I immediately got to work trying to scrape together new travel funds. I wanted to get back on the road as quickly as possible. Far from putting me off, what I had been through convinced me that I was an *adventurer*, a hardcore one. I was more confident. I knew the route and all its traps now. And above all, I knew for certain that the third attempt would be the successful one. Three, a man's number.

CHAPTER 5

When I met Paul-Emile Latour-Genets, I had lost all hope of making something of myself, honestly or dishonestly, either by going back to my gang of impetuous thieves or by attempting once again to get out of this stinking backwater. I understood that after two failed attempts, I was forever damaged goods. Nobody wanted to invest again in this old horse who wasn't even capable of reaching the finishing line. 'I almost made it,' I repeated in vain. The more sympathetic ones listened to my whole story before politely sending me away. Others shrugged their shoulders as soon as I started my refrain. No purses opened up.

Paul-Emile, alias Elgep, was a humanitarian of the luxury sort. Like many others, he was in Africa to help, but not to help those destitute who gratefully jump to hug you because you have distributed soap or lotion samples raided from hotel rooms. Neither had he come on behalf of any NGO, begging there to play philanthropist here. Elgep was a stand-alone donor using the overflow from his bulging pockets. He was well born. Several generations of his family, of old Avignon bourgeois stock, had occupied high-office functions. His grandfather and his father had both been lawyers. An only child, he, to his father's despair, had left for Paris to further his studies. He then had a brilliant career as a bank executive. Coddled by destiny, Elgep lived contentedly until a tragedy shook up his world. At the age of sixty-six, he lost the love of his life in a terrible car accident. Shattered, he suddenly found his retirement – which he had planned to dedicate to love and leisure – pointless. Idle and rolling in dough, he decided to give back. He was looking for a noble cause when he bumped into his college friend François Dubray. Elgep had just left his apartment on Avenue de Lamballe in Paris's XVI arrondissement to spend a few days in his country home in Apt, Vaucluse. He was filling his car's tank when he caught sight of François, his blue scarf eternally wound around his neck, coming out of the petrol station shop. At the shop's counter where they had a coffee, François summed up his life of adventure.

Unlike Elgep, François came from a family of penniless aristocrats who clung to their chateau in Maine-et-Loire as the last rampart of their glorious past. Following their law studies (at which both he and Elgep had excelled), François had joined the Ministry of Foreign Affairs. He arrived in Africa very young, first as a diplomat. He then joined a UN agency before creating his own development NGO. Separated from his first wife, who was unable to adapt either to the climate or to the indiscretions of her spouse, François married an African and thereafter felt liberated from all need for diplomacy or courtesy when hurling about his home truths to lazy Africans, incapable of pulling their continent out of the rut of underdevelopment. His insights sometimes bordered on racism but when one tried to point this out to him, he brandished his licence to criticize: 'I remind you that I am married to a black African!' Black, he insisted, in case his interlocutor assumed he had sought a wife from the extreme north of the continent or among the whites in the extreme south.

With precious advice from François Dubray, Elgep arrived in our country with a very simple idea: to build top-level vocational training centres for young adults failed by the conventional school system. It was evident that the problem of this country, like in all of Africa, whose development quest had borne no fruit, was linked to a lack of qualified technical workers. To solve the problem, infrastructure was needed to train these workers for development. In one year, he had two superb complexes built, one in the south and the other in the north of the country. He had discovered the two regions thanks to François Dubray, who had entrusted Elgep to local friends. François was a long-time developer. He believed he knew the specific problems of every one of the fifty-four countries that made up the continent. He presented himself as a specialist of several, not daring to admit that he had not visited all of them. Elgep's intermediaries in Ouabany had not contradicted their friend François. Education, they affirmed in chorus, is truly the key to development. They were not wrong. But instead of guiding their new friend through the meanders of the administration in order to obtain the necessary permits and, above all, align with national plans and curricula, they claimed that this could be taken care of later. 'Once the buildings are built, "they" will be obliged to use them,' explained Gorgadji and Nazinon. They each rushed to take him to their home region. In the north, as in the south, Elgep was welcomed like the Messiah himself. MPs made the trip from Ouabany. Traditional chiefs, local administrative officials and all kinds of civil and military authorities applauded him for having chosen their region. The local inhabitants in both regions were mobilized to welcome this friend to their region in an official ceremony complete with speeches, dances and manifestations of public jubilation. 'Jobs are going to be created, your children are going to be trained. Your region was selected to host this auspicious project,' declared the mayor in the north. A bit dazed by all the flurry, but flattered deep down that his gesture had been met with such gratitude, Elgep let himself be carried along with the general fervour. When he got back to Paris, he released the first instalment of funds. A joint account had been opened in a bank in Ouabany with Gorgadji and Nazinon both named as account holders. From errand boy to architect, from day labourer to construction firm, Gorgadji and Nazinon called on brothers, cousins, nephews and friends to partake in this endeavour honouring their home region. A few inflated invoices, a little embezzlement and some deadline extensions later, Elgep was once again the star of two ceremonies orchestrated to hand over the keys to the buildings. Sincerely moved and fully in the flow now, he also made a speech in which he promised that once the administrative formalities were completed, 'These buildings will reverberate with knowledge and enthusiasm, enthusiasm for contributing to the development of the region, of the country, and, why not, of the whole of Africa!' His speech was met with wild applause.

A year later, what was supposed to have been a mere formality had become an insurmountable obstacle. Called on for help, François Dubray managed to put a word to his highly placed friend, the transport minister. This minister was not on very good terms with his colleague from National Education. They had fallen out over a grim episode involving the distribution of offices between their two ministries. Nonetheless, the transport minister had tried to raise the issue through a small note he slipped to his counterpart during the ministerial council.

He wrote: 'It appears that you have at your disposal two fantastic complexes in the north and in the south to strengthen the supply of education.'

His colleague responded: 'I'm aware of those anarchic constructions that took no account of our ongoing policies and plans. This is not a jungle!'

The transport minister could do nothing more to resolve the situation. Denouncing his colleague to the prime minister would only put himself in a difficult position. He had, in fact, just been in the spotlight for having allowed the importation of one hundred reconditioned buses from the fleet of a European municipality without the approval of the council. While it had not been formally mentioned, rumours of corruption and pocketed bribes hung over him. He'd had his wrist slapped. His colleague's use of the word 'anarchic' was not casual. The same adjective repeatedly punctuated the rebukes of the prime minister, who was eager to show his firm hand to the president of the republic, the boss of them all.

The two beautiful complexes built by Elgep thus shimmered in the hot sands of the north and in the lush green forests of the south, empty and useless! During each trip, Elgep saw his accomplishments being eaten up by sand and wild weeds. Gorgadji and Nazinon, on the lookout for new friends with new projects, had little by little abandoned him. They still responded to his phone calls, and even organized working lunches with solemn-faced office employees who promised the moon and the sun and then disappeared as soon the lunch bill was settled by Elgep.

The disappointed donor was thus going through this ordeal, and I was going through mine. We had nothing in common and we were not destined to meet each other. But chance knows the most tortuous paths to change your trajectory.

I was beneath the people. The lowest of the low! I was from the fourth world. Not the third, but the fourth. I had actually tried to get a job with the NGO Fourth World Destiny. One morning, between various attempts to escape my rathole, I dropped in to see them. 'Sir, Madam, I would like to make myself useful, to work for the eradication of extreme poverty.' It was the seventeenth of October, the International Day for the Eradication of Poverty, and an open day had been organized to plead our cause. I had expected an enthusiastic response: 'Welcome! Take a seat, we have been waiting for you. Thank you for joining our movement.' Far from it! Several other 'fourth-worlders' had come before me and there were no more spots available. Plus, they must have understood that it was just a strategy, a step toward an escape. And yet it was Jean-Yves, a purebred Frenchman, who gave me the idea; he had arrived in our country this way, in the opposite direction. He proposed his services to a similar NGO on another seventeenth of October. The NGO had warmly lauded him for his civic commitment to fight world poverty. At the time, Jean-Yves was jobless and hated, above all, the cold winters in his native Franche-Comté. What cruel fate, to be born in Mouthe when you shiver at the slightest wind. At eighteen, with his high school diploma in his pocket, Jean-Yves moved north to Paris, focused more on seeking warmer climes than knowledge. A single Paris winter and a disastrous semester at Jussieu

University, and he decidedly concluded that it was preferable to pursue his quest for warmth in the south – much further south. One evening, sitting in our *grin* tea group, Jean-Yves thus related the circumstances of his emigration to me. He was sure that my own emigration plan would one day work if I joined a similar NGO. 'Offer to volunteer and take the time to win their trust. Sooner or later, an opportunity for a trip will come up and you can take advantage of it.' It appeared so simple. I was surprised that more potential migrants hadn't thought of it. When I went to see Fourth World Destiny, I realized that this avenue, like so many others, had already been fully exploited. Western embassies' visa services now asked NGOs for exorbitant guarantees and made them sign a form claiming responsibility if someone travelled to Europe on their behalf and disappeared once there. I was desperate.

My sister Marité had a friend whom I could not bear to look at, and yet Rokia was a real beauty. She was Fulani with smooth dark skin, delicate features and long wavy hair. I had been madly in love with her and had written her dozens of my most impassioned letters. She simply ignored my passion. No scorn, no rude or exasperated response; just indifference. I had tried unsuccessfully to break up her friendship with Marité to get revenge, but Marité and Rokia had been close since the start of junior high, and now, in the third year of economics, they were still inseparable. For some weeks, a nice car with green number plates dropped off Rokia whenever she visited my sister. The driver left if the two planned on staying together long, or waited if the visit was a brief one. Curious, I had asked Marité about the car and she explained that Rokia had quietly married a Swiss UNICEF employee. 'They will soon go home,' she added. 'Go home where?' I asked stupidly. 'I think the place is called Aubonne.' Marité gave me all the details.

Quentin, the blushing groom, was retiring and had decided to take over the family vineyards in the small Vaudois village, not far from Lausanne, where Rokia planned to continue her studies. I was furious! So she had spurned my vigorous young arms to seek refuge in the soft comfort of the flaccid flesh of this Swiss fellow? When she asked Marité to see if I would help them move, I almost strangled myself. But my sister has always known how to soften me up, and she got me to agree. In reality, it was just a matter of sorting through their things and sending some furniture and boxes to Rokia's relatives. Marité and I also inherited some trinkets. Then a team of professionals came to pack and send everything off in one day. On the last evening, a gentleman showed up to visit the house, intending to take over its lease. Quentin greeted him and showed him the interior and the garden before the landlord arrived. Everything seemed to the liking of the future tenant, who suggested that he come the very next day to collect the keys. The plane for Switzerland was leaving that same evening, so Quentin – whom, despite everything, I liked well enough (maybe sincerely or maybe with ulterior migratory motives) – asked me if I would stay until the next day to hand over the keys. I accepted, happy to escape from my father's new season of admonishment for a while. My father had got into his head the idea of sending me to the village to live with my uncle Joanny, the chief.

'You can help him in politics,' he said. My uncle presided over the local section of the ruling party.

'But Benoit and Emile are there!' I exclaimed. Benoit and Emile were my cousins.

'You know very well that they haven't been to school. You could even be a candidate in the upcoming district elections,' added my father.

'Leave my son alone,' my mother dared to intercede. 'You who were born there, *you* did not want to go back. Him, he's a child of the city! And then, those people with their *juju*!' My father glowered at her, but didn't say anything. He would come back to the argument later. That was always how it happened with those two.

In the meantime, I was happy to spend the night in a calm place. I set up my foldable bed on the veranda, enclosed by mosquito netting. The next morning, I was awoken by bird-song. The pink villa was submerged in lush greenness. The whole garden was a forest of potted plants, huge trees and lianas that climbed the tree trunks, wrapped around poles and spread across the cast-iron frame of the veranda's roof. A bore-hole allowed for unrestricted watering. There was even a small waterfall, the continuously running trickle creating a pleasing sound. Around eight in the morning, Monsieur the New Tenant arrived, and that is how chance – or destiny, its other name – brought Elgep to my path.

CHAPTER 6

Pain, like wine, ferments. After reading Marité's email about our father, I remained prostrate on my work table until morning. That is where Elgep found me awash in my pain, mixed with shame and remorse. Was it really my fault? Had I killed my father? I asked my questions out loud and Elgep, compassionate, shook his head before pulling me off my desk. 'Go and rest,' he said simply.

That is Elgep. Very sparing with his words. He would do without them if they weren't indispensable. It had been the first thing I noticed when he arrived at the villa to pick up the keys.

I had been waiting for him outside, under the shade of the cashew tree. When I saw the car approach, I opened the gate that led to the garage. Monsieur Latour got out, came toward me and held out his hand wordlessly. I had planned to give him the keys, collect my camp bed and get out of there, but everything happened as if it was understood that I was to stay in the house.

At the end of the day, after I had accompanied him to luxury shops, street kiosks and city markets to buy furniture, bedding, utensils and dishes, he said: 'We had better shower before going for dinner. Take the guest room.' The driver, Samuel, had left in a taxi to pick up his motorcycle from the hotel Elgep had checked out of that morning. I wanted to escape, complaining that I did not have clean clothes to change into. 'Go and get some and come back. You know how to drive?' I didn't. That was no bother, my new boss or friend – I didn't quite know what to think of this new relationship – held out a ten-thousand-franc note. 'Take a taxi. I'll wait for you. But hurry, I'm starving.' Less than an hour later, I was back with a sports bag containing a few hurriedly grabbed clothes. During dinner at Le Manguier, we sealed our friendship and an unusual contract in a few words. 'I need a friend who knows the country and can help me with my formalities. I will pay you two hundred thousand francs with room and board.' That was his proposal and I accepted it.

I quickly became an efficient and indispensable assistant. I also essentially became the governor of the pink villa. Mr Ranini and Mrs Ninda, the watchman and the cook, submitted their lists of expenditures for the house's upkeep to me. Elgep insisted that they be addressed as mister and missus. Ranini, who had served Quentin, was happy to have kept his position. As for Ninda, she was a distant cousin of my mother's. When she had arrived in the city, like others from her village, she dropped off her bundled belongings at the home of my maternal grandparents, where my uncle Adrien has lived since their death. Her marriage had led her to our neighbourhood where she grew closer to my mother, especially following the death of her husband. I knew her to be an excellent cook. She had been trained by the sisters of Our Lady of the Apostles and cooked for the parish priests before she got married. My mother puffed with pride when she called Ninda over to offer her the position. Not only had her son found work but he was now also employing others.

My bedfellows in misery, no longer seeing me hanging about our street or wallowing in front of Modou's screen, came looking for news. Having learned of my good fortune, some came to me when I passed through to visit my parents. Could I not find something for them too? I now had my driver's licence and drove Elgep's Jeep Grand Cherokee. Nobody asked me what I did as a job. 'He works for a white!' The formula was magic. For us deplorables from the outskirts, to work for a white man like Elgep was to get close to the Holy Grail and its boundless abundance! My own parents didn't enquire about the nature of my work. Initially they just supposed that I was his houseboy. I don't think that would even have bothered them. But when I got Ninda hired as a 'domestic assistant' (the term used in the first article of the contract that Elgep had drafted in due form), that is, responsible for cleaning the house and preparing meals, they guessed I might be his secretary. Even in the public sector, more and more boys were choosing this profession that, in the past, had been reserved for girls. 'And what salary is he getting?' asked my mother with a rhetorical flourish, her circle of friends and visitors suddenly much larger. 'Forty thousand, fifty thousand? Jeanphi is making two hundred thousand francs a month!' she concluded amidst admiring and envious oohs. In a few months, I transformed the family home. The mud-brick wall, half of which had eroded away, was replaced by one of cement. The house was entirely repainted in a martial blue, my mother's choice. She also requested a grotto, which I had built in a corner of the courtyard. In it she placed a statue of the Virgin Mary that the parish priest came to bless with great pomp. My father was more reserved, as if to punish himself for not having believed in me, but I felt that he was just as proud as my mother. Only Marité appeared intrigued by this good fortune, as unusual as it was sudden. She invited herself to the pink villa to meet *Elgep the Fairy* as she called him. A single debate on I don't know what topic of economics, and she became an enthusiastic admirer of *Elgep the Erudite*. From then, she was regularly invited to dinner, alone or with friends from university.

Nina (Ninda rejected the *d* in her first name, having lost it in the baptismal fountains of the Our Lady of the Apostles church) impressed Elgep with her know-how. He had little by little initiated her in a more refined cuisine, more to his taste, all while congratulating her at every meal. The two got on like a house on fire and on evenings when we expected guests, they would lock themselves up in the kitchen from four in the afternoon. In the midst of clanking pots, we would hear their murmurings punctuated by bursts of laughter. Around six, sweet smells would permeate the house, and Elgep would come out to bathe and prepare to receive his guests. He was very well groomed. At almost seventy years old, he was well preserved. While not really thin, he had known to avoid the portliness so common in those people his age who did not suffer from malnutrition. He was a fine gourmet with no qualms about treats even when no guests were expected. 'How about a nice little feast this evening?' he would ask when, for one reason or another, he was in joyous spirits, his eyes gleaming, their grey colour seemingly turning blue. Thus, Elgep was someone who lived it up all while watching his figure. 'There's no question of letting the structure fall to ruins,' he would say after one of his excesses, putting on his tracksuit to go for a run around the lake near the house.

In addition to Marité and her friends, Elgep hosted some of his compatriots, avoiding others whom he called *petty bourgeois whose farts escape from somewhere higher than their bottoms!* He, who was not usually verbose, could not say enough on the topic of these *arrivistes.* The people he did receive shared the same opinion and asserted their distance from those *pretentious* and *snobbish* circles! They affirmed that they had come to help, not take advantage. Most of them worked with NGOs. Sometimes locals, recommended or accompanied by Nazinon or Gorgadji, also visited. From our first encounter, I had pigeon-holed those two as big-time swindlers. How could such an intelligent man like Elgep have placed his trust, even for a second, in such scammers!

The dinners with students were the liveliest. Elgep knew how to provoke them or push them further into their entrenched positions with just a few words. Smiling slightly, he then listened to them debate tenaciously, contradicting and defending their ideas. Only Marité, who understood his game, would not let herself get pulled in. My naturally curious mind sharpened through exposure to these eclectic debates. My old dictionary was no longer sufficient, and I started to regret the early interruption to my studies.

Elgep hadn't given up on opening his two vocational schools. I helped him with the administrative procedures that were at a despairing standstill. I suggested we try another avenue. With an enormous white rooster and an envelope containing some cash in hand, we went to call on my uncle, the chief. I had sent word to him, and he received us as distinguished guests. When we arrived, he was seated on a wood-sculpted chair under the

enormous baobab tree next to his palace. Dressed in a large
boubou in local white handwoven material, and a red bonnet
with multicoloured diamonds on his head, my uncle had an air
of great nobility. Village dignitaries surrounded him, seated on
mats or directly on the ground, with their caps in their hands
or humbly placed beside them. I was very proud to introduce
my friend. After the long customary greetings, I handed the
presents over to his page, who was kneeling to his right. I explained the purpose of our visit. I took care to speak in our
language, so as to honour my uncle. For him, as for my father,
the French language was a trophy of war brought back in their
soldiers kit. They kept it and manipulated it with great liberty,
colouring and mixing it up at will, but in his role as chief, my
uncle only used the local language. When I finished, he addressed his dignitaries, summarizing what I had just presented
and adding his own comments. The elders listened to him,
emitting sounds of acquiescence: *hon hon, woto bala!* From their
happy expressions, I could tell they appreciated our approach.
A son coming to seek support from his *senior father* to help a
friend – a white no less! – now *that* was music to the ears of
these respected custodians of tradition. I almost burst out
laughing when I thought about the expression my uncle had
used. A literal translation would be something like, 'Grab the
behind of his senior father!' The traditional gesture when asking for someone's help to avoid danger was to grab them by the
waist and tightly wrap your arms around them. The person
thus girdled was obliged to help you, and the more powerful
the person, the better they could protect you. That a young
man of my age had taken such initiative, and especially for his
foreign friend, impressed them. They said as much to my uncle, who looked at me proudly. They pretended not to know

that it was less the village chief and more the local head of the ruling party who I had come to solicit.

A few days after our visit to my uncle, the party president, who had spoken to my uncle, met with us. He then contacted the minister of national education who gave us an appointment, just before he had to fly off for an overseas mission. We came out of our meeting reassured and confident that our imbroglio would have a happy ending. Things would finally become unstuck. A few weeks later, the minister's cabinet summoned us for another meeting with the grand commissioner of the state. He received us, somewhat tensely, in the middle of his immense office, and made the following proposal to Elgep: the Ministry of National Education would accept the buildings and take the buildings turn them into comprehensive middle schools, given that there were not enough vocational teachers for the two complexes. Elgep tried to counter by offering to fund training for the necessary vocational teachers. 'Where will you train them? And who will do it?' asked the minister. 'We have neither the higher training facilities nor qualified teachers to lead them.' The serpent was biting its tail. We left the minister's office completely depressed. For the first time, I felt that Elgep was at his wits' end. The minister's attitude puzzled us. During our first meeting, he must certainly have been aware of the insurmountable obstacles he was just now presenting. I promised Elgep I'd get to the bottom of the minister's about-turn. It was my uncle who provided the explanation. He explained to me that even if the prime minister and the party president were from the same ruling party, they couldn't stand each other. Specifically he said, 'They do not borrow fire from each other.' The minister of national education could not implement his promise without the approval of the prime minister, and the latter started fuming when he learned who was recommending the project. How dare the party president interfere in matters concerning the executive of which he was the head? The education minister had then rushed to his office to summon us and backtrack on his promise. We tried in vain to reach the office of the prime minister. Tired of the battle, Elgep transferred the buildings to the ministry as suggested and decided to return to France.

CHAPTER 7

Comfort is a drug that enslaves quickly. It was just a year ago that I moved into the enchanting pink villa. Yet I had the impression that I had always slept in an air-conditioned room, in a big soft bed. Having a bank account that was never in the red seemed the most natural of things. Eating, not just to satisfy my hunger but also my whims of the day, going to the cinema, to restaurants, as I wished, living without worrying about tomorrow all quickly became habit. Above all, I had become accustomed to the respect and deference that people showed me. All that was about to collapse.

When it was clear that the prime minister would not meet with us, Elgep announced his decision to return to Paris soon. He liked his social life in Ouabany, but the experience of the aborted project had disappointed him, and on top of that, he had a lot of difficulty adjusting to the climate. Two months after I moved in, Elgep had told me he needed to go back to France 'to sort out some issues', as if he was embarrassed to admit that he wanted to avoid the peak of the hot season. He left me in charge of the house, the employees and all running matters. Apparently I did a good job, because after that he never hesitated to return to France every once in a while to 'resource himself' as he called it. This time, however, it was to be a definitive return. 'Not definitive,' Elgep tempered. 'This country and its people are now a part of my life. I have friends here whom I'll never forget. I'll come back to visit,' he said. I believed him. After a year of living together, I trusted this man completely.

At first, I had been wary. That first evening, when I accepted his invitation to dinner and then later to sleep in the guest room, I did so with suspicion. For a while, I looked for the catch, convinced that there must be one. This man couldn't place his trust in me so suddenly that he would invite me under his roof from day one.

One evening while at dinner at Le Manguier, I asked Elgep about the reasons for his spontaneous generosity toward me. 'Generosity?!' he exclaimed. 'It's not generosity!'

'But you took me in without knowing me,' I insisted.

He explained that he had learned of my financial struggles from Quentin, who had been informed by Rokia. He hadn't promised anything to them, having barely glimpsed me the evening before. 'When I saw you arriving at the villa the next day, I had no doubt. I knew I could trust you.'

'Without knowing me?'

'Yes,' was Elgep's only response.

I didn't enquire further, but promised myself I would return to the question. But then came the earthquake that almost toppled everything.

Elgep was very discreet about his private life. He had only told me that he had lost the love of his life in a terrible accident. I understood that he didn't want to dwell on such a painful episode of his life, therefore I never talked about it. It was he who would sometimes let slip slivers of memories: 'Chouchou loved chocolate' or 'Chouchou and I used to do this or that ...'

Some days the remembrances of this happy past filled him with sadness, and he remained holed up in his room refusing all contact. When he came out, he would be distant for hours as if in a daze. I respected these moments of melancholy, as did Nina. She would serve our meals in a grave silence. Once, while we ate in such silence, I caught Elgep looking at me in a way that made me uncomfortable. I immediately lowered my eyes, hurriedly finished eating, excused myself from the table before the meal was over, and went for a walk along the lake. I was much intrigued by that look. It was not the lascivious look of the unknown man from Myriam Makeba Avenue. This look was, one could say, less carnal, more profound, more delicate. It was a kind, benevolent look. Why had it bothered me? When I got back to the villa, Nina had left and Elgep had retired to his room. The next morning, fearing a confrontation, I got up early, hoping to leave before Nina arrived and, above all, before Elgep awoke, but when I walked into the kitchen to make coffee, he was already there.

'Do you want a coffee?' he asked jovially.

I could not refuse.

'Excuse me for yesterday evening,' he said spontaneously. 'It's because there are moments when you remind me of Chouchou.'

'I remind you of your wife?' I asked incredulously.

'My late companion,' corrected Elgep in a calm voice.

Bringing the cup to my lips, I paused and set the cup back on the table. In a flash, the meaning of Elgep's look was clear to me. It was the gaze of someone in love! Without a word, I went back to my room and locked the door twice. I grabbed a bag and randomly threw in my things while Elgep banged on the door. When I came out, he tried to take my arm, mumbling excuses I didn't hear. I threw him a look that made him drop my arm and immediately stop talking. I left the house without a word.

I flagged a taxi. 'To the Kremlin!' I told the driver. I didn't know where to go. I didn't want to return to my family home. I would have had to explain why I had left such a well-paying job. So I chose the Kremlin, a bar recently opened by Robson – or Robert Songré by his real name – a friend who had returned from the United States against his will. There I could cool my boiling anger and think things through more calmly.

So, I had been living under the same roof as a *fag* all these months? I hadn't noticed anything, suspected anything. There were some signs that should've warned me though. Elgep never mentioned Chouchou's real name, and some of the female students in Marité's group had tried, in vain, to ensnare the handsome sixty-something-year-old in their youthful nets. Then there was the matter of Christelle! The pretty brunette who came to dinner at the pink villa one evening and fell under the charms of Elgep. Elgep had firmly rejected her, and she sought consolation in my arms. The following morning, Elgep was steaming mad when he saw her coming out of my room. At the time I attributed it to jealousy. Opportunities were not lacking, but I hadn't seen him grab any, out of what I thought was loyalty to Chouchou. And what's more, he had just celebrated his sixty-ninth birthday. I assumed that age had diminished his sexual needs.

I arrived at the Kremlin as the cleaners were finishing up. Small Paul, the barman, arrived shortly after and let me in. I hung about until early afternoon, and then called Christelle to join me. I needed a sensitive and sympathetic ear. Christelle promised to be sensitive, but refused to be sympathetic. She advised me to go back to the pink villa and talk to Elgep.

'First of all, what makes you think he wants to sleep with you? Has he ever come on to you in all these months?' Christelle asked.

'No, of course not! But I can't live with a *fag*!' I replied.

'So you're homophobic?' she retorted, giving me a scornful look.

Christelle couldn't take me in, not even for a night. Our relationship had been too intermittent and she had ended up giving up on it. She now had a long-term boyfriend who lived with her. She left, repeating her advice to me: 'Go back and talk to Elgep.' Instead, I ordered a cognac. I rarely drank alcohol. Every once in a while, I had a nice glass of wine with a meal, but never more than that. Even beer, so loved here, especially during the hot season, didn't tempt me. I hated the eructation it caused. The first cognac got me drunk, but I ordered more, and downed them in hasty gulps. I ended up collapsing on the counter. Robson called Elgep to take me home. The next morning, I awoke in my bed, and like a coward, I sunk back into my mattress and slept until noon. Nina brought a tray with my food and told me that Elgep had had to leave on a trip. He had left an envelope.

Dear Jeanphi,

Do you remember the expression in your language which you translated for me once? 'To be born with'. There are things that one does not choose. I did not choose to be born homosexual! I was born one. From childhood, I knew I was different. When I became a teenager, I understood what that difference consisted of and it was a source of suffering for me. I wanted to die. And then, I learned to accept myself. When I came out to my parents, my mother screamed about sexual perversion. My father threatened to kick me out. In the end, they thought it more discreet if I stayed under their roof. I left for Paris after my baccalaureate exams. At the time, the issue was still taboo, even in Paris. But it was easier to hide there. Twenty years later, a young man named Guy Hocquenghem published a letter coming out as a homosexual. His manifesto started a revolution for homosexuals in France. We came out of hiding, but still made sure to be discreet. Homosexuality was still listed as a mental illness when I met Stephen (Chouchou). He had come from England under the pretence of his studies, but above all to hide his particularity. We fell in love and decided to move in together. Our love saved our lives. AIDS killed most of our friends.

And then came the terrible accident that killed my happiness.

I never lied to you. I always talked of the love of my life, of Chouchou … never of my wife. One learns to hide things without lying. My sexuality has nothing to do with my charity work. I didn't come here to find a new companion; you know that well. Your friendship is dear to me. Do not let one unfortunate look spoil this precious link we have. It is your friendship I want, Jeanphi. Not your body.

I am in a hotel in town. I will wait for your call. If you decide to leave, give your keys to Mr Ranini. I will come back on Sunday evening.

Sincerely, Elgep.

I folded the letter, put it back in its envelope and tucked it under my pillow. I stayed in bed that whole Friday. Nina, believing I was sick, was very attentive to me. She was only supposed to work a half-day the next day, a Saturday, but she stayed until evening, when Mr Ranini arrived. I still hadn't come out of my room. I was in complete and utter confusion. The most contradictory ideas battled in my mind. And in particular, one nagging question kept circling back: Was I gay without knowing it? What signals was I giving out to attract all these *fags*? Elgep was the third man to find me to his liking. In addition to the dirty white guy from Myriam Makeba Avenue, there had also been a rich Moroccan who'd turned a refugee camp in Nador into his secret harem. His henchmen would round up young guys to present to him under the pretence of recruitment.

He had arrived, one day, sat in the rear of his posh car with tinted windows, and pointed to the ones he liked. I was chosen. The rich man left, and his men prepared me. Hammam, manicure, pedicure, hairdresser; I was cleaned up from head to toe, dressed in new clothes, and in the early evening driven to an inconspicuous apartment in the outskirts of Oujda. When I asked them where they were escorting me, the two henchmen said that it was for an interview with the boss for a butler position. Knowing the prevailing racism toward us, the hygienic preparations had not really surprised me. A young woman served me tea and cakes in the sitting room where they took me, and then disappeared. The boss came in, dressed in a large sky-blue gandoura, all smiles. 'What's your name?' he asked. When he sat down, not opposite me, but right next to me on the couch, I finally understood what the whole ignoble masquerade was about. I leapt from the couch and hurried to the door. His men, alerted, moved to stop me, but the boss spoke to them in Arabic and they let me go. Once on the road, I cried with a mixture of shame and rage. I felt dirty and humiliated, not only by the desire of that *lech*, but by the whole cleaning operation that had preceded it. When I reached the camp around midnight, a welcoming committee was on the lookout. Seeing me return on foot, completely downtrodden, they understood that I had not yielded to the old pervert's couch. Bertrand, the chief of our section, told me that he was aware of what was going on.

'And you didn't report him?' I had asked outraged.

'To whom? He is very powerful and we are illegal. And anyway, only newcomers or those who are interested fall into his trap. He doesn't force anyone,' he explained.

'Those who are interested?' I asked.

'Yes,' continued Bertrand, 'some yield to the desires of that sex-hungry man. None of them remain in the camp afterward because we do not tolerate any *fairies* here! That's all that we can do.'

I burned my new clothes and took my place within the group again. No gibes nor insults disturbed my peace. And now once more, I was desired by a man. And not just any man. My relationship with Elgep had got to the point where I was ready to place him just after my parents and Marité. More than a friend, I considered him a second father. Could I still trust Elgep?

I had never been sexually attracted to another boy. When I was young, people often found me cute. I was almost as tall as my father, but I inherited my mother's fine features, particularly her long curled eyelashes and the gap between her two front teeth. Whose fault was this pleasant physique? I *was born with it* too. But I liked girls. Elgep knew this. He saw me, more than once, take a girl to my room in the pink villa. Elgep had never shown his disapproval, apart from with Christelle. I had remained quiet about my private affairs because I hadn't yet found the girl I wanted to spend my life with. Moreover, I was in no hurry for such a decisive meeting, given I had not abandoned my dreams of escaping. Thinking about Christelle again, I now understood Elgep's anger. She was capable of offering me the same things as him, and even more, if we fell in love.

She could open to me not just the doors to her villa, but also to her country, Belgium. He feared that she would snatch me away from him!

On Sunday morning, I finally came out of my room. Mr Ranini had left and Nina did not work on Sundays. While I was eating breakfast in the kitchen, the doorbell starting ringing insistently. I picked up the intercom. It was Marité. I opened the gate.

'You look terrible!' she cried as she entered. 'Are you sick?' Without waiting for my reply, she asked to see Elgep, urgently.

I thought I would get rid of her when I told her he was not in. She insisted, saying that her professional future was on the line. Her application for a local position at the UNDP had been shortlisted and the interview was scheduled for Monday.

'And you need Elgep for your interview?' I asked, a bit surprised.

'According to my sources, the guy who will be interviewing regularly has dinner here,' she explained.

'Pulling strings does not work with white people,' I objected.

'Are you kidding me? Whom did we learn it from then? *The art of winning without being right!* You remember?' retorted Marité. I frowned in puzzlement, and she added: 'Cheikh Hamidou Kane. Did you not read him? It's at their school that we were formed, malformed and deformed!'

I called Elgep, who arrived half an hour later. After Marité left, Elgep and I went to Le Manguier for lunch. He swore that nothing would change between the two of us and that from now on, *he would rather poke his eyes out than embarrass me again with ambiguous looks!* He kept his word. I was wary the first few days. I always put a few metres of security between him and myself. Easy-going, he remained as he was before the incident.

Sometimes I got the impression that his smile was mocking my distancing precautions. And time, the adversary of memory, ended up doing its job. The memory of that improper gaze faded, and the malaise that grew out of it slowly dissipated. I ended up seeing Elgep as I saw him before. And yet, I couldn't shake the idea that there must be something abnormal in me too. Obscene images started filling my mind.

At first, they were flashes, which I waved away like annoying flies. And then they became increasingly persistent, more prolonged. When they invaded my nights, I decided to seek the help of a priest. I had been a regular at Sunday Mass until adolescence. My parents wouldn't have had it otherwise. They themselves were very devout, especially my mother, a member of the Legion of Mother Mary, to whom my sister and I owed the 'Marie' in our first names: Marie-Thérèse and Jean-Philippe Marie. I had freed myself from the chore of Sunday Mass ever since my time on the streets, despite my mother's pleas. Confronted with the intrusion of devilish images in my thoughts during my waking days, and sleeplessness during my nights, I asked Nina for the name of a trustworthy priest. She recommended Father Isidore at Our Lady of the Apostles. This affable and welcoming man of God met with me and entrusted me to one of his exorcist colleagues. And this colleague, convinced that *attraction toward the same sex is a developmental disorder which is both treatable and preventable*, recommended that following two deliverance sessions, I return to *a chaste life following the teachings of the Catholic church* to counter my satanic thoughts. I followed his advice and returned to the church. It brought me a certain serenity. In vain, I doubled up my efforts to help Elgep open the two schools.

CHAPTER 8

Some mornings I am tempted to be courageous. To dare to upset the order of this unjust world. To dare to do something that reconciles me with myself. Something that would most certainly interrupt my tranquillity, or worse, bring troubles upon myself. I think of what Rosa Parks did that first of December in 1955 in a bus in Montgomery, Alabama. By refusing to give up her seat to the white passenger in front of her, as obligated by state laws, this civil rights activist knew what she was risking. But she did so anyway. I watched a documentary on her life. The reason for her act of audacity: *I was tired!* Physically tired, as is often the case after a long day of work, but above all, tired of submitting. Tired of giving up her place as if her own tired legs were made of wood! Would I ever have such courage? For the moment, my old friend, laziness, kept me nailed to the sofa, the same sentence repeating like a chorus: *This life is not mine!* A vestige from my tormented nightly dreams, this refrain obsessively filled my mind from the moment I awoke.

The day before, invited by a perfumer friend, Elgep had gone to Grasse. Alone at Tourelles, I had all the time in the world to unravel the thread of my life all the way to this corner of France where I had arrived a few months earlier. I had unspooled and spooled the thread again, twisted it in all directions and concluded: *This life is not mine!* To busy myself and be rid of this sterile refrain, I tidied the old newspapers covering the coffee table. A headline grabbed my attention: 'Expatriation: The Countries Most Attractive to French Youths.' The article commented on the results of a survey in which young French people interested in *expatriation* were asked about their preferred destination. Most had chosen those English-speaking countries that were among the largest in the world. 'The American dream is still alive,' concluded the journalist. The word *expatriation* intrigued me, especially as a few pages later in the same newspaper, another article lamented 'the tragedy of illegal immigration': 140 sub-Saharan African nationals, dead from thirst in the Libyan desert. I opened the dictionary. I needed to clear up this linguistic mystery. Why are some people *expatriates*, while others *migrate*, *emigrate* or *immigrate*? Reading the various definitions just confused me further. The words had almost the same meaning. *Expatriation* means you migrate to another country. When you leave, you *emigrate*, and when you arrive, you *immigrate*. And then a detail jumped out: in French, one expatriates oneself, *s'expatrier* – that *s'* changes everything. Expatriate oneself, a pronominal verb *conjugated with a personal reflexive pronoun*. I expatriate myself: I have held conference with myself, weighed the pros and cons and decided to deport myself elsewhere! This is a choice: an act of will, not of fire under your bottom. When I migrate, I do not have a choice. It is the winds of poverty or of war that push me out of my home. And then I ride the waves of struggles, driven by contrary winds, thrown against reefs of iron and laws that reject, never sure that I will arrive safely to port.

I had recently taken up studies again, distance-learning courses to prepare for the baccalaureate exam. One of my history lessons was on European emigration to other continents between 1870 and 1910. They had also *migrated, emigrated, immigrated*, pushed by hunger, poverty and violence. And today they *expatriate themselves*! I picked up the newspaper again and looked carefully at the photo illustrating the article on expatriation: a young woman photographed from behind, sitting on a suitcase in the middle of an immense road. In front of her was an open horizon, onto which a white world map was superimposed. She could close her eyes and blindly choose her destination! Very few countries would be shut off to her! From Africa, the countries that are easily accessible can be counted on your hand. In the end, I had succeeded in migrating, but at what cost?

Elgep left Ouabany three months after handing over the two buildings to the minister of education. The ceremony took place in the minister's offices; he gibbered a long speech, the only audible part of which was on *these philanthropists from the other side of the world, who show concern for us and our development, make enormous sacrifices to contribute to the education of our children,* et cetera, et cetera ... He then, *in the name of the President of the Republic and by virtue of the powers vested in me*, hung a Medal of the Order of Merit on Elgep's chest. Elgep had tears in his eyes as he thanked the minister. Whether he was moved or disappointed is anybody's guess.

Elgep had a six-month rent deposit on the pink villa. He proposed that I take advantage of the deposit, as well as of all the furniture he left behind, while I found my feet again. *Find*

my feet! That was the expression he'd used. Find my feet where
and how? Return to the family home once again? Rent a
smaller house until my savings run out? Or hope to find a
good job by then? Pay an agent to attempt the crossing one
more time?

I had to decide. But, as often happens when I am over-
whelmed, my inclination toward procrastination took over. Ah,
how I like that word: *procrastination!* I fell upon it by chance
one day when leafing through my old dictionary. From then
on, we never left each other. We got on so well together! I
spent long weeks chilling at the house, reading, watching TV
and dreaming. There would always be time to decide tomorrow, I said to myself. I even neglected Sunday Mass, where I
had become a regular following my exorcism.

Improper images like idle minds. They came back, at first
confused and diffuse. Then they became more focused, and involved my dear Elgep in their naughtiness. I did not really no-
tice when the threshold was crossed. I surprised myself one day
murmuring: 'After all, why not?' What is a small black ass
worth compared to being poor? If mine could serve as my
passport to Europe, why not? There would always be time to
return to healthier companionship later. As soon as I conceived
the inconceivable, I spent entire nights listing all that my
sacrifice would allow me to save. One year of Elgep had lifted us
out of the brackish waters of penury: my parents no longer
strung to the rhythm of the three-month payout, my sister had
just signed her first contract with the UNDP, and I had become used to the comforts of the pink villa. All of that could
continue. All of that depended on me.

One day I would be ready, and the next would find myself
cowardly and shameful!

All around me, relatives and friends were waiting for me to announce my departure for Paris. Elgep had maliciously let slip this possibility to my father when he went to say goodbye. My father had rushed to spread the news. People gazed at me with admiration. Marité came to check on me and found me slumped and depressed. 'Still no visa?' she asked teasingly. I was about to confess to her my turmoil. But how do you speak about the unspeakable? Why involve my younger sister in a responsibility that was mine to bear? I kept quiet. A few days later, a week before the lease expired, I conceded. I sent an SMS to Elgep: *Okay, I agree.* I had no doubt he would understand. He understood.

He wired me a tidy sum to extend the villa's lease until I obtained my visa. A few weeks later – with his letter of invitation that included the description of his luxury Parisian apartment, my bank account that he had taken care to swell, and the credit card the bank had rushed to give me – obtaining a tourist visa was nothing but a formality. My second-ever flight was in business class. After a night travelling in comfort, I found Elgep waiting for me at Roissy Airport in the early morning hours. It was late autumn. Far from the sparkling city that I recalled from TV, Paris appeared sad in its foggy aura, its buildings grey and trees naked.

CHAPTER 9

Which came first, the chicken or the egg? An old riddle that
has never been solved. I looked at the hate-filled face of
Palamni and another puzzle came to mind: Which engenders
the other, malice or jealousy?

We were at the Ouabany airport and I was getting ready to
check in for my first trip to Paris. Relatives and friends had
come out in droves to witness this miracle: someone from their
lot was extricating themselves, lawfully, from the worthless
gangue rock. There was much buzz, talk and laughter. And
then, the last call for check-in. I had to go. Just as I was about
to pass through the metal detector, Palamni arrived – suppos-
edly to say bye – squeezed through the crowd, grabbed my
neck and hissed in my ear: *You are off to join your husband?* I
couldn't do anything. The other travellers were already pushing
me through to the security zone. I turned around, powerless,
to see him mock me. He was smiling with all his false teeth,
waving goodbye with his right hand, while his left, held at
chest height, gave me the finger. Pure malice is a sight to be-
hold! I barely knew him. With his small and stocky frame,
Palamni walked like a crab trying to escape a boiling pot. His
reputation as a brute was well established in the neighbourhood. He was not my age-mate. A bad student and a trouble-

maker, he'd already been kicked out of school by the time I started. But he spent his days under the shade of the African mahoganies with the women selling bread with sauce, our favourite snack at recess. He terrorized my classmates and me. We were victims of his extortions until the day Mister T., head honcho in the neighbourhood next to ours, punched Palamni in his ugly mug, breaking all his teeth (well ... maybe one or two were left). At the time, a neighbour, Ténin, *the voice of honey*, ridiculed him in a song during a naming ceremony that spoke of a toothless *head bandit*, whom everyone recognized as Palamni. We hadn't heard anything of him for a while after that. Then he reappeared with that artificial smile that reminded you of the Cheshire Cat in *Alice in Wonderland*. Why had he gone to all that trouble to hiss such a murderous phrase? How had he guessed? *What if he was one?* Elgep had suggested this when, still troubled by the incident, I related it to him. He explained that there was no greater homophobe than a repressed and frustrated homo. I was ready to believe it, seeing how sudden and derailing the accusation had been. Until then, nobody had found it suspicious that I lived in the pink villa with the *old white man*. Back home, boys wore bright colours, held hands or lived together, without anyone suspecting them of being homosexuals. Given Elgep's respectable age, people saw him above all as an adoptive father to me. Was Palamni particularly lucid?

Most rumours have no father nor mother. The poor orphans are thrust about from a malicious mouth to a willing ear. It is impossible to retrace their progenitor, in order to oblige them to swallow back down their incestuous work. There are rumours, however, that are signed works. Shortly after my departure, the neighbourhood started whispering timidly: 'Have you heard the news?', 'They say that ... ', 'Apparently there's something fishy in Jeanphi's move!' Those who had seen me off at the airport felt betrayed. They tried to find out more and, in doing so, spread the rumour further. The whispering became a murmur of indignation and then an explosion of anger. Baba Péré, whose mouth wore neither thongs nor briefs, as they say, felt obliged to bring up the matter with my father – it was unfortunate, for him. '*Prinka, prinka,* here comes Pepin the Short!' my father would moan whenever the old man pushed open the gate of our compound, mocking his rapid, jerking gait and smaller-than-average stature. My father some-times listened (or pretended to listen) to Baba Péré because al-though tired, like everyone else, of the verbal diarrhoea of this old man who was not *altogether there*, he thought it best to let him babble on until he ran out of steam. As long as I could re-member, my father always had little patience for mongers, both of wares and of rumours. He quite bluntly rebuffed both, not leaving them any opportunity to display their treasures of junk. I imagined my father in his rocking chair – one of his last whims I had catered to before leaving – face covered with his panama hat, responding without a doubt with 'Oho! Oho, oho's when Baba Péré launched into his gossip: 'You know what people are saying?' My mother, busied by some house chore, had paid them no attention until the explosion of her husband's voice. The old chatterbox fled like a rabbit. Gener-ally, my mother pitied Baba Péré. 'The poor man', she would often sigh upon seeing him. '*When you cannot hold your feet, you must know how to hold your tongue!* The ancestors taught us that.' He controlled neither one nor the other. Nonetheless, she would welcome him with benevolence and offer him a bit of food. But on that day, she decided to shut the door to him de-

finitively. Perhaps she would continue to pray for him in between her supplications for souls in purgatory.

The slander of their son rolled off my parents like water off
a duck's back. 'Let them braaay!' my father said to me on the
phone, guessing that the hubbub of jealous saboteurs with
crocodile eyes may have reached me. This is how I started my
sojourn in Apt with the blessings of my father. A few days after
my arrival in Paris, once Elgep had taken me to see some of
the unmissable sights of the capital, we had headed out to this
small Provençale town. To Elgep, the estate he had inherited
from his parents, Tourelles, seemed the ideal environment for
me to adjust to my new life. His parents, in their old age, had
left Avignon for this beautiful residence, an old farmhouse built
between the courtyard and the garden, situated majestically on
a hillside, where they spent fourteen years under the shade of
its big lindens. When her spouse, Pierre-Henri, passed away,
Hortense Latour-Genets had preferred to retreat to a retirement home, where she passed away soon after.

Elgep and I spent autumn and winter by the fireside, well
protected from indiscreet eyes. Yvette, the housekeeper, who
was still sprightly despite her seventy years, worked four half-
days a week; Wednesdays were reserved for watching her
daughter's children in the centre of Apt. She lived on the other
side of the courtyard, beyond a small wall bordered by a row of
cypress trees. The rest of the time, Elgep and I remained alone,
receiving very few visitors as we preferred to meet Elgep's
friends in bars and restaurants in Apt. Once or twice, unexpected visitors would disturb our hibernation.

Such was the case one Sunday afternoon, when Yvette
brought the parish priest and the vicar from Saint-Anne's
Cathedral to see us. The old lady, who never missed Mass, had

earlier discovered that the vicar was my compatriot and suggested introducing us. Not very excited by the prospect, I kept putting off the date until she came ringing our bell with the two men in tow. I immediately recognized him, even without his cassock. Father Daniel, a native of Wego, a small village a hundred or so kilometres from Ouabany, was a reserved, almost shy man. By what miracle had he ended up as vicar in Apt? 'It's the work of the Holy Spirit!' proclaimed the more talkative priest. Father Dominique was a joyful joker, with a juvenile face and a monk's tonsure. Father Dom, as his parishioners called him, had almost been excommunicated for a passion that the bishop had deemed devilish. Father Dom was a fan of metal – heavy metal music, that is – and had dared to express this publicly. The Black Angels, a Norwegian band, had played at a heavy metal festival in Nîmes once, and at the end of the concert, a journalist, intrigued by his black collar, approached Father Dom and asked to interview him. Discovering a veritable music lover, the journalist spotlighted he priest in his coverage, almost costing Father Dom his parish and his cassock. Elgep told me this story after our visitors left. Curious, he had tried to meet Father Dom at the time but without any luck. The bishop had sent Father Dom to a holiday camp while the whole affair calmed down.

A few days after their impromptu visit, the vicar returned on his own to Tourelles and asked to speak to me. Elgep left us alone near the fireplace. Father Daniel, with no oratory pre-caution, entreated me immediately to leave the life of sin I was living. Shy people are like pressure cookers, you see. Every-thing is kept under pressure and when the valve opens, all the steam gushes out. I let him unfurl his sermon without saying a word. He explained that therapies existed to help people like

me. Aside from exorcism, a Catholic psychiatrist could help me
uncover and understand the deep underlying emotional trauma
that gave rise to this unnatural attraction. Because, of course,
there must have been some kind of trauma to cause this satanic
behaviour. While he had spoken in French, I responded in our
native tongue: 'But Father, *I was born with it!*'

Shocked, he *shook the sand off his sandals* and never again set
foot in Tourelles. I am not sure how it happened, but it was
through him that my father received the first serious alert as to
his son's deviant behaviour. On the phone, he simply asked if I
knew Father Daniel, a fellow countryman living in the same
region. When I admitted having met him, my father stayed
silent a long moment and then hung up. Fearing the worst, I
called him back the next day. He never again alluded to the
priest, but his calls petered out and then ceased altogether. I
was only able to talk to him by calling my mother, who had received her mobile phone. She reassured me: 'You know him!
He is no longer enchanted with his new toy and doesn't even
charge it!' I chose to believe her and continued my tranquil life
in Tourelles.

As soon as spring brought out the first buds, Elgep shook himself off and decided that it was time see Paris again. This second visit reconciled me with this town, a long-time subject of
fantasies, which had so disappointed me on my arrival a few
months back. Elgep introduced me to the magic of Parisian
nights. I was so seduced that I tried to convince him to move
to his apartment on Avenue de Lamballe. He had the wisdom
to resist this temptation to drift and abandon ourselves to the
party life. I never would have been able to finish my studies

otherwise. The calm and serenity of Tourelles enabled me to pass my *baccalaureate* exams two years after my arrival and start another distance-learning programme in project management.

Although they were only occasional, our stays in Paris and outings in *gay* bars – the word still scorched my mouth – allowed me to meet an endearing cosmopolitan fauna. That is how I became friends with Lisa, a gorgeous mixed-race Brazilian with an almost perfect resemblance to Liz Taylor. I met Lisa one evening when her melancholy blues had cast her down, she who was usually so luminous, so sparkling. She was sitting at the end of the bar, snapping at anyone who tried to approach her. Feeling a little nostalgic for the place I had tried so hard to leave, I had gone out alone that evening and sat down on the opposite end, also chasing away all who seemed to want to come near me with a simple look. The two poles of resistance ended up noticing each other. It was Lisa who crossed the three or four metres separating us. She spoke to me of Salvador da Bahia better than all the guidebooks and documentaries put together! She made me penetrate the soul of that mythical town, strolling down the steep *ladeiras* of Pelourinho or her neighbourhood of birth, Cruz do Pascoal with its colourful facades. She took me to Rio Vermelho on the beach. I closed my eyes, listened to the lapping of the waves and saw little Francisco sitting on a low wall near the boats, dreaming of his future life as a woman, as she confided: *I never doubted that one day I would be a woman!* I raised my eyes in surprise, but didn't say anything. With a small mocking smile at my astonishment, Lisa continued her trip through São Salvador da Bahia de Todos os Santos where she seemed to have left half her heart. She was an extraordinary storyteller. She even managed to carry me away to Candomblé ceremonies among entranced worshippers. I shuddered when she spoke of the orishas. Yes, I, the African, trembled listening to this almost-white woman talk of the wrath of gods directly imported from the Yoruba pantheon!

'I was born during a Candomblé ritual,' Lisa explained. 'My mother was only fifteen and, despite her condition, my grandmother insisted on her presence to finish her initiation as a future lalorixa, a *terreiro* priestess according to the will of Lemanja, their house's orisha. My mother's water broke during the dance of the divinities. There was no time to take her out of the terreiro. I was born in the corner of the room while the ceremony went on.'

I could have listened to Lisa the whole night. But after an hour of her flamboyant accounts, she lifted her green eyes to me and whispered in a rushed tone, 'And you? Where do you come from? Tell me!' I have always lacked eloquence. That evening, I stuttered some clichés about Ouabany, and then, confused, I concluded, 'Some neighbourhoods are just like how you've just described Salvador.' I wasn't aware of how true this actually was. I visited Bahia a few years later and, wandering the streets, I felt like I was back in Ouabany. My friendship with Lisa started as an antidote to our melancholy and gloom at a bar counter in the Marais. It lasted less than a year, brutally interrupted by a raving madman who savagely murdered my friend out of amorous resentment. It was an odious crime that made newspaper headlines. A few months before her murder, Lisa had confessed to me her fear of the man, who claimed to have left everything – wife, children, job, social standing – for her beautiful green eyes. 'I didn't even sleep with him, Jean-phi!' she had exclaimed. 'I haven't asked anything of him; I haven't promised him anything!'

Lisa met Sebastien on one of her depressed evenings, a little bit like the night we met. 'What was he doing at La Mutinerie anyway?' Lisa asked me, exasperated by her suffocating lover. 'A mutineer from the heterosexual aristocracy?' I listened to her as usual, impressed by her glibness but also a bit alarmed when she recounted how Sebastien followed her everywhere and fought with the men she brought home. Lisa had just broken up with her lover, Ernesto, when I met her. She hadn't found another stable relationship and was floating around. No doubt, that's why she hadn't hesitated to seduce Sebastien with no intention of going further than that blow job in the restroom at La Mutinerie. But for him, the experience had been a revelation and he offered to leave everything and shack up with Lisa. 'You're joking Coco?' she had retorted, amused and a little flattered by his eagerness. He wasn't joking, and did actually leave everything. Driven crazy by Lisa's indifference and mockery, he killed her and cut up her body, placing parts in numbered plastic bags that he kept in his freezer. Did he eat some of her body, as some newspapers claimed? I never had the courage to think about it.

Before her atrocious death, Lisa filled me with an irresistible desire to set foot on the Brazilian soil so precious to her heart. Elgep organized our first trip to Salvador de Bahia to celebrate our civil union under French law, a kind of honeymoon. We loved it and returned regularly. During our fourth trip we decided to venture further toward Nordeste Brazil, which was said to still be wild. It was a fantastic experience. Instead of the planned three days, we ended up staying two weeks in a small corner of paradise called Jericoacoara, *there where crocodiles sleep in the sun.*

CHAPTER 10

There are two types of women: those who require nothing to look good and those who look bad in everything. I watched Rama come toward me, draped in a black printed sarong, and decreed her a worthy representative of the first category. She had crossed two strips of the light cloth over her chest and tied the ends behind her neck. Perched on high-rise platform sandals, she moved forward airily across the sandy beach, defying the laws of balance.

Rama was my lifebuoy and I think I was hers. Under the pressure of the tumultuous gushes of our lives, we clung to each other so as not to drown. She was the first black person I saw when I got off the bus in Jericoacoara. When you are in minority, whatever resembles you first catches your eye. I understood immediately that Rama was from Africa. There were other tanned faces in the street, some lighter, some darker, but the pretty ebony tone and the wax-print dress were familiar to me. We were staying in the same *pousada* and, the very evening of our arrival, the four of us — Rama's companion David, too — climbed the Por do Sol Dune to admire a magnificent sunset.

There was an immediate complicity between Rama and me. As in a mirror, we had both recognized the other. There was no need for words to understand what we had fled and where we had landed. It was all written on our fresh young faces and on the rather less fresh faces of our companions. Well before we told each other our stories, we knew everything about our destinies, so distant and so close. Lives of survivors. Our lives of constant bad weather, through which we lurched about, trying to navigate without keeling over at every little wave. 'We need to remain afloat despite the pressure,' Rama would say to me. 'Do you know Archimedes' principle?' I don't know where she learned it, but when she explained it to me, it seemed obvious! Well ... not the first time. 'It is a force that pushes upwards, and that acts on objects that are submerged in fluid, water, air ...' she started. 'Huh?' I asked. I had always been allergic to scientific matters. My mind, which was so permeable to the poetry of words, remained hermetically sealed to theories or words that attempted to demonstrate realities so clear they became obscure. Did I need to know *why* boats float on water? They float, and that was enough for me. However, Rama was not a woman to be satisfied with what seemed obvious. She was a seeker of sense. She liked to rummage, to probe, and sometimes went a great distance to find answers. Like this Archimedes thing!

'Have you never wondered how ocean liners made of steel do not sink?'

'Yes, of course,' I retorted.

'Well, that's what Archimedes explains. The king presented him with an impossible task: to check that his jeweller had not cheated him by exchanging some of the gold in his crown with silver. How to go about finding this out without destroying the crown? Archimedes thought about it day and night. Illumination came to him in the public bathhouse, and he ran out, naked as a worm, shouting his solution in the middle of the road! Any body submerged in water is subject to force. If the force is greater or equal to the weight of the body, it floats. If not, it sinks. You have to find the point of equilibrium to float. You get it?'

All I understood was that to keep our heads above the turquoise waters of Jeri, to hope to float on toward better tomorrows, we had to find balance every day, in our bodies and in our minds. *Mens sana in corpore sano,* Rama liked to repeat. Each morning, she insisted we walk along the beach, before the ever-growing crowd of tourists invaded this lost paradise. Our companions were respectful of this early morning seclusion. It was our moment, our time for confidences. We would wander along the beach, telling each other about our past miseries, our present dreams. Rama was trying to get David to marry her, while I was wondering whether or not I should undo my civil union and escape from this paradise. Sometimes, Rama took off her sandals and we ran about like kids. We would fall to the ground, and in a fit of giggles, roll to the tip of the waves before getting up. Today, I tell myself, I could have, or even should have, fallen in love with Rama. We could've run off, got married, and we would have straightened out our lives. But the problem with love is that it has no helm. It is difficult to steer in the direction one wants. Beautiful Rama was, and remains, my best friend, my confidante, and nothing more.

'I have been crying for so long, Jeanphi!' she confessed to me during our first walk. 'Nobody knows, especially not David. Some mornings, I have to wrap ice in a kitchen cloth and put it over my puffy eyes. Then I put on my day cream and my make-up and the mask is on. I come out smiling, and no one is none the wiser! If I were white, I would have seen a specialist a long time ago. I would have been diagnosed as depressed, or even worse, and I would be downing a ton of pills or wallowing in an asylum! But I am a proud African woman. Certain pains must be kept in your belly. They are too scared of the wind that carries them to malicious ears. My mother used to say that pain, once exposed, attracts vultures.'

Rama cited her mother ten to twenty times a day. She described her to me as a woman who was always even-tempered. Never a word louder than another. Even her laughter she smoothed, like a grain seller smoothed out their piles of grain. Nothing was ever in excess, except her love for others, which her very being radiated: her calm, her eyes sparkling with tenderness, her enchanting smile. That smile had conquered the heart of her future husband, Seni, when he caught sight of her in the small grocer's on his way to buy curdled milk. It was the month of the Muslim fast, and Seni was returning from his bicycle shop to buy some treats. He knew the small grocer's well, but it was the first time he had crossed those clear eyes, that ravishing smile. Disconcerted, but only a half-hour away from the break of the fast, he fled the source of temptation. In the days that followed, he regularly stopped at the grocer's, but only found the two youths normally in charge of the cash register monitoring the shop. A week after Eid-al-Fitr, he asked the older of the shopkeepers the identity of the ravishing smile. 'Mademoiselle Alima? She comes here only rarely. The boss does not want her here,' the boy explained.

Seni spared no effort. He used the neighbourhood imam to arrange to meet the boss, Alima's father. He then had to conquer the beauty, who dreamed of returning to the coast where she was born and had attended school until her father brought the whole family back to his hometown of Ouabany.

But Alima hadn't taken well to Oubany's dry air, and she took even less well to her father's refusal to put her back in school. Not being the type to rebel outright, she attempted persuasion. On the cusp of turning eighteen, she had finally got permission to visit her aunt on the coast when Seni entered the scene. Love softens the harshest climates, and she consented to the marriage. But when she learned that two other women had preceded her in the home, she baulked. Seni was able to convince her that no woman preceded her in his heart. His first wife was the widow of his elder brother, and his second had been imposed on him by his father. He promised Alima an exclusive love. He whispered to her, *You are the one I have chosen!* Seeing how they cooed, Seni's two co-wives, who until then had fought each other every single day, reconciled and came up with a thousand plots to separate the lovers – to no avail. After the forty days of honeymoon with his new wife, Seni tried to establish equity in his relations with the three women, but was never quite successful. Alima inspired faith through her discretion and calm under all circumstances, and her husband was drawn to her, entrusting her with his purse and his secrets. This sharpened the hatred of her rivals who teamed up against the favoured wife.

They bewitched her, Rama claimed, convinced that her mother's death had not been natural. 'You don't die from simple colic! They killed her!' The premature demise of her adored mother changed the course of my friend's life. I don't think she would have set foot in Jericoacoara if her saint of a mother had lived a few more years. An excellent student, Rama dreamed, at the time, of getting her science A levels, and a scholarship and a spot at a prestigious university. Her mother had laughed at the enthusiasm of her darling, without ever dissuading her to the contrary. She never used Rama's birth name, assigned by virtue of when she happened to be born. *My darling*, a term even more precious in their language that few mothers used, rolled off her tongue like a caress.

Coddled by a soft and loving mother and a father who was just as doting, Rama had a protected childhood that even rivalries, jealousies and dirty tricks in her polygamous family hadn't troubled. Her mother had always intervened, and patiently neutralized any arrows directed at her daughter. Alima died when her daughter was embarking on the difficult years of adolescence. Her two co-wives transferred their enmity onto the offspring of their deceased rival. Without maternal protection, the young Rama was outmatched. She tried in vain to get her father to referee but, mad with the pain of his loss, her father remained deaf to her appeals for help. Rama ended up leaving home with a sunken heart, knowing that her two younger brothers would now be subjected to the malice of her two stepmothers and their children.

How do you survive on the streets at sixteen? To avoid being found, Rama had gone to a very touristy small town on the coast, and after a year of this dissolute life, she met David. She was seventeen. He was fifty-eight. But he was the first to offer her a more stable life. 'Ten years already, we've been together,' concluded Rama. 'You want a *pastel*?' she added a bit hastily, no doubt afraid that I was going to ask her questions after the peek she had just offered under her life's veil. 'Have you tasted a *caipirinha*?' she asked, dragging me to the small multicoloured *barracas*.

That first trip to Jeri left me with a distinct taste. The sweetness of living tinged with bitterness. It was there, more than anywhere else, that I really became conscious of the dead end my choice had led me to. I still hold on to the nostalgia of that sense of suspended time, the sentiment of total abandon prompted by the seclusion of that place. I could do nothing at the time. So I revelled in the umami taste that my meeting with Rama, and our shared confessions, made all the tastier. It was she who, once again, found the right words to express what I was feeling. 'To have someone to whom you can say that things are not fine! It seems simple but it is so rare. We want to remain dignified, walk with our heads held high, and so we silence our wounds, our suffering. I searched for a long time before meeting you, Jeanphi. You are more than a friend. You are the other me, whom I can tell everything. It is not everyone who finds their alter ego, whether in love or in friendship. Promise me that we will always stay in touch.' I promised. We kept our word.

Two years later, during another trip to Jeri, Rama left David. Tired of waiting for him to overcome his children's resistance and marry her, she fell for the charms of Guillaume, a young Quebecer passing through. Both in love, they left Jeri in haste, leaving us to care for an inconsolable David. Elgep and I had a lot of difficulty taking him back to France.

A few months later, I received a nice photo of the wedded couple under a red maple tree. Written on the back was 'Happy at last!'

CHAPTER 11

The immensity of the sea is made up of drops of water. A single drop counts. And a single drop is within my reach.

The American Indian legend goes: *One day there was an immense fire in the forest. All the terrified animals looked on, petrified by the disaster, powerless. Only the hummingbird did something, fetching drops of water with her beak to pour onto the flames. After a while, the armadillo, irritated by the pitiful agitation, said to her: 'Hummingbird, are you mad? It is not with drops of water that you are going to put out the fire!' The hummingbird responded: 'I know, but I am doing my part.'*

I read this story for the first time in a brochure I picked up one Tuesday morning at the Apt farmer's market. Christine, from whom I had just bought a leg of lamb, asked me: 'Do you know these guys?' No, I responded, should I? 'One of them worked in Africa, in the Sahel.' I was now integrated, with a light southern French accent, and I was no longer shocked when people thought me to be omniscient, that I was expected to infallibly provide answers on any subject – science, literature, geography – related to Africa. *How many inhabitants does Lesotho have? What is the GDP of Burkina Faso? And Botswana, how big is it?* Based on my skin colour, I was the designated expert on African issues. And when I didn't know something, which

happened frequently, people turned from me as if I was igno-
rant. *What kind of African is this who doesn't even know his own
country!* In the beginning, I would get annoyed, I would
protest: *Africa is diverse! It is a continent with fifty-four countries!*
And then I learned to smile at their ignorance. Christine's
question was very specific as it concerned just the Sahel, a band
of land crossing Africa west to east, from the Atlantic to the
Red Sea! Also, she was kind and full of useful tips for tenderiz-
ing a leg of lamb! With a large smile, I again shook my head.
'Here, read this!' she said, handing me the brochure and turning to her next client.

When I got home, I in turn handed over the brochure to
Elgep without a word. After reading the Indian legend with an
ironic tone, he scrunched it up and put it in the bin. I rushed
to take it out, but he stopped me: 'If you want to join a citizen
movement, go and see the SCA.' The SCA? 'Yes, Solidarity
and Citizen Action. I used to contribute to their activities.
Their office is in Avignon.'

A few days later, he drove me there, introducing me to the
world of grassroots movements found across France, Europe
and the world. Ordinary citizens, particularly women, were
active in these movements at the crossroads of charitable and
political work, tired of the inertia and incompetence of central
powers, and wanting to influence local affairs, to restore social
bonds and solidarity. 'Put the citizen back at the heart of
democracy!' proclaimed one. 'Don't wait for someone to do it,
we are the makers of our well-being. Act now!' incited another,
echoing Kennedy's inaugural address: 'Ask not what your country can do for you, ask what you can do for your country.' How
loud and inspiring that voice from America had been!

SCA taught that each citizen, whatever their position in society, had the skills, to contribute to progress in their society, to
reinvigorate democracy. I sought out some of the agents of this
citizen spring. I attended a conference by Josuah Divrai, that
semester's leader of SCA. I came out transformed! There are
some people, who in just one meeting, shine the light on your
path in life. One single conference opened my eyes: I had to
do my part, like in the Indian legend! I, too, could bring a
stone to the construction site back in my homeland. After a
sleepless night, I was lit up by the idea that I absolutely had to
return to Ouabany with a social project. Aside from the conference by Josuah, in Avignon I had also attended a workshop
on non-violent communication. The facilitator presented it as
such: *Learning how to interact with others without violence.* He de-
veloped an entire chapter on *empathy*, at the heart of this type
of communication, which was studied very seriously by emi-
nent researchers in big universities. *This approach aims to develop
a life ethic founded on empathy, compassion, self-respect and respect for
others in order to achieve a peaceful society*, he concluded. Exactly
what I needed to re-establish contact with myself and with
those close to me.

Lately, I tended to wallow in guilt, to take upon me all the sins
of Jeroboam. Ever since my father had died of shame,
according to the diagnosis of his neighbours and friends, I
teetered on the brink of depression. I thought of nothing but
returning home, and would have done so immediately, if my
mother and Marité hadn't put me off. They were scared I
would be attacked. Seeing that this argument did not have
much effect on me, they subtly let it be understood that they

would be uncomfortable if I came home so soon. For months I prowled impatiently, endlessly tormented by the same unanswerable questions: *Was it really my fault? Had I killed my father?* I was no longer sleeping. My nights were so agitated that I left the marital bed.

Elgep and I were the first gay couple to get married at the Digne-les-Bains town hall. When we came back from Jeri at the beginning of November 2012, we fell straight upon the first large-scale demonstration against same-sex marriage. The movement had just started its crusade. Elgep was enraged, and I had to hold him back to stop him from venting his anger at the demonstrators. It was shortly after that Elgep suggested we get married if the same-sex marriage law was passed. Which it did in spring 2013. I remember that Friday, 17 May 2013. We were in Tourelles, as Elgep could no longer stand the highly agitated environment of the capital, polluted by both pro- and anti-same-sex marriage squabbles and demonstrations. I was in the kitchen when I heard him shout. I rushed to the living room where he was watching TV. 'It's done! The law has passed. We can get married!' He was jubilant. While he had never joined any gay rights organization, Elgep considered himself an old activist for the cause. He had witnessed the main evolutions and revolutions in this fight for existence. This last victory really seemed to excite him. I expressed to him my surprise that people *like him* were fighting to access an institution as conventional as marriage. *Like us*, he corrected and then explained to me why 'marriage for all' was not a retrograde battle. After the battles for recognition and freedom would come the battle for equality. 'That is the final victory. When we are no longer just tolerated, but have the same rights!'

A few days after the law passed, Elgep repeated his request. I hesitated a few weeks before consenting. Getting married wouldn't change anything in our daily lives, and our civil union had already enabled me to get a French passport several years ago. I was doing it for him, without really taking measure of what it would cost me.

On Thursday, 12 September 2013, accompanied by two friends, we stood before the mayor of Digne-les-Bains, Elgep stylish in an impeccable beige suit, and I, a bit intimidated, almost shameful, in a navy-blue suit, my neck covered by a silk scarf. We had gone to another district in order to be discreet. Elgep's parents had bought an apartment in the pretty thermal town and had regularly spent time there to treat Pierre-Henri's rheumatism. Since Elgep now owned a property in the district, we were legally allowed to marry there. Moreover, Elgep knew the mayor and knew he wouldn't refuse to celebrate a gay union like some other mayors had.

Despite our precautions, a local paper had sent a reporter, alerted by the prospect of a scoop. A few days after the ceremony, Yvette, whom we had not informed of the marriage, brought us a copy of the local edition of *La Marseillaise*, with a nice photo of us on the front page. Whether she told Father Daniel or whether he came across it in the paper himself, I don't know. What I do know is that it was through him that the photo reached my father and put a definitive end to his doubts. That killed him. A few weeks after the sad event, he stopped talking. Apparently, his last words before the onset of his final mutism were the ritual formula of my banishment. It was my cousin Benoit who told me this with glee. My mother, whom I asked to confirm this terrible information, didn't deny it, but assured me of her blessings and prayers. I had needed training at the SCA centre to learn the principles of non-violent communication. My mother had been practising it for years by instinct. She had guessed my life choice well before my father. Having assured herself that it was a free choice, she'd accepted it and I'd never felt as though her love for me suffered.

If all parents were like my mother, my project wouldn't be needed. But I knew that most parents were more like my father, ready to vilify any offspring practising sodomy. I had recently read an article online about the violent expulsion of a small community of homosexuals from a Ouabany neighbourhood. One young guy was killed by his own father. That tragic story strengthened my conviction that I had to do something. When I brought up the idea of creating La Goutte d'Or, Elgep gave me precious advice. He suggested that in order to avoid gays being stigmatized, I open the centre to all struggling youths. La Goutte d'Or should be a *space* where together we would find solutions for each person depending on their needs. As the project took shape, Elgep became more and more enthusiastic, thinking the wound of his failed humanitarian work was finally starting to heal! I had to use all the techniques that I learned about non-violent communication to inform him that I didn't want to return to my country with him. He pretended not to be hurt, continuing to contribute to the project with the same energy. He drew my attention to a series of tragic events that had befallen sub-Saharan migrants on the Libyan coast. His press review related the numerous drownings as well as the extortion, sequestrations, assassinations and other violations of the rights of those men, women and children fleeing misery and the threat of terrorism by hundreds. The route that I had taken a decade ago was still being used, but more were attempting to pass by the Libyan route now. One newspaper explained that since the fall of Muammar Gaddafi, Libya had fallen prey to incessant battles for power and was plunged in complete chaos. Migrants who managed to survive the dangers of the desert now found themselves trapped in this chaos. Elgep's new idea was that La Goutte d'Or be open above all to youths wanting to take the road to exile. 'You must inform them, Jeanphi,' he pleaded. 'Their lives depend on it. Agents are lying to them.'

Elgep's idea was also based on a very practical consideration. He was convinced that a project aiming to inform young Africans about the dangers of emigrating to Europe would easily find funding. He was not wrong. My proposal was welcomed enthusiastically in Brussels. The fund manager agreed to sponsor the construction of the first building to incite me to start as quickly as possible. 'We never do this,' he insisted on specifying. 'We fund activities, not property investments. Consider this an exceptional gesture of support. The gushing flow must urgently be stopped! All these young people risking their lives!' As if he cared about the fate of those unfortunates or their countries of origin. If such was the case, then why waste millions of euros on improbable and ineffective military operations? The Mare Nostrum Operation, launched the previous year, had cost more than nine million euros each month for a veritable anti-immigration armada! And Frontex? The ineffectiveness of such *bunkerization* was behind the new interest in initiatives like mine. I was aware of this, but *he who begs, shuts his mouth!* Therefore, I shut mine and got back to my preparations.

And then I had to tell Elgep my decision to leave him. None of the methods I learned were soft enough to communicate a break-up in a non-violent manner. Elgep knew that the success of the project depended on me moving to Ouabany. Yet he continued to talk about our future as a couple. Was he betting on my inability to readjust to the precarious living conditions that awaited me? Or was he hoping that I would end up accepting that he would join me? The thought of a break-up certainly didn't seem to have crossed his mind. As for me, I kept beating around the bush.

Finally, one day, I knew the boil had to be burst. When it's time, you just know. You don't ask yourself why, you just know. And that day, it was time. I already pitied him, poor Elgep. He did not deserve this. Nobody deserved this. I knew his attachment to me was sincere. He took the blow and made me promise to not start any divorce proceedings for now, and continued to prepare my return to my home country with enthusiasm that was not feigned. Finally, the big day arrived.

CHAPTER 12

'What is a small black ass worth compared to being poor?'
Jamal murmured, hand on the doorknob as I was getting ready
to dismiss him. The same sentence I had mumbled one fateful
morning before sending the SMS that had changed the course
of my life. I turned around and faced him for a few seconds.
His face was so close to mine. I felt a terrible desire to take his
cheek in the palm of my hand, to kiss those lips offered by way
of provocation. I could've done it. It was what he was
expecting. I held myself back. His insolent glare reverberated
with the same question. Not much, I thought. I had offered
mine to escape a life of struggle. Elgep, who was genuinely gay,
who had come out of the closet forty-five years before our
encounter, knew very well that it was not my sexual
orientation. He liked me; he chose to believe in the sincerity
of my about-turn. But today, could I still maintain that I had
no taste for *it*? The turmoil that every sight of young Jamal
triggered in me. The repressed urge to take him in my arms, to
kiss him, to place my hand on his small, tight ass. No one else,
man or woman, had ever stirred such ardour in me. Jamal
measured me up, a light smile on the corner of his lips. He'd
understood, the smart-ass. He knew I liked him. He, clearly,
liked boys. He told me so the day of his very first visit. He had

been rejected by his family, didn't know where to go, and was
trying to emigrate, whatever the cost ...

We had taken him in for some weeks at La Goutte d'Or,
but spots were few to come by and the length of stays was
limited. After he exhausted his stay, I had been able to get him
a job as a waiter at Bread Potato, a restaurant belonging to my
friend Irene, a Haitian who'd landed in the middle of the
Sahel. Jamal didn't last a month. His mischievous look and
impeccable dress had at first seduced Irene, but she quickly
discovered the other side of the coin. Insolent and mocking,
Mister Know-It-All had annoyed his boss with his sarcastic
comments about how her restaurant was run. In consideration
of our friendship, Irene took his behaviour in stride and most
likely wouldn't have fired him. But after yet another
confrontation, it was Jamal who quit with a bang. This was
what he'd come to tell me, begging me to take him back at the
shelter, even suggesting he share my quarters, *so vast for just one
person!* But what did he want from me? I was a married man.
Elgep had obstinately refused divorce. We were separated but
he remained convinced that I would come back one day. Once
you have tasted comfort, you don't easily do without it. He
doesn't say this, but he thinks it and he isn't completely wrong.

I had almost turned back as soon as I arrived in Ouabany.
Getting off the plane, I had taken a step back, dazed by the
wave of heat. The hostess, thinking that I had lost my balance,
grabbed my arm. I smiled at her wordlessly and started to go
down the stairs. Marité was in the arrivals hall. She drove me to
Desert Rose, a modest boarding house not far from the airport.
We had agreed that I would not stay at my mother's, given the

general hostility toward me in our neighbourhood. I had also
turned down the offer from Marité and Guy, her boyfriend, to
host me in their flat in the city centre. Desert Rose was situated
on the road to Kogrin, the new development where I had
secured the land to build La Goutte d'Or.

From the very first days, the harshness of life in Ouabany
made me regret my nonchalance when Elgep had tried to convince me to change my departure date. 'April is the peak of the
hot season, wait for the first rains,' he'd advised. In my haste to
return to my beloved land, I hadn't listened; I was born there, I
retorted, making small of the thermal shock. I thus arrived
right at the peak of power cuts and, even worse, long water
cuts – forty-five degrees under the shade and not a single drop
of water! Each day, on my way to Kogrin, I passed by women
in search of the precious liquid. I admired their ingenuity. They
transported enormous jerrycans on the ends of yokes tied to
their bicycles. As soon as construction started, I commissioned
a borehole and allowed those women to come and pump water
there; the water was purer than what was so scantily distributed
by the utility company. This gesture bought me goodwill from
the neighbours and the women from the informal settlements
bordering our new neighbourhood. From dawn, multicoloured
jerrycans would be lined up in front of the small gate, waiting
for it to be opened by Mr Beogo, the watchman. Living conditions in Ouabany were perhaps no worse than when I had left;
they had probably even improved. But they were still onerous,
especially during the dry, hot season. In my nostalgic mind I
had idealized my motherland, remembering only its more ad-
vantageous sides. I had also, no doubt, thought that a little bit
of penitence would help my quest for rehabilitation; but the
task proved to be harder than I expected. With the rigours of

the weather, the slow pace of bureaucracy and the hostile welcome in my childhood neighbourhood, the beginning of my
project was marked by challenges. More than once, I was on
the brink of giving up.

The evening I arrived, Marité and Guy had driven me to
my mother's. She hadn't aged much, but her gaze, which used
to sparkle so, had lost its shine. The following day, I had
expressed my wish to pay my respects at my father's tomb in
the village, where my uncle, the chief, had had him buried.
My uncle had tried, without success, to add our mother to his
harem, but Simone, supported by her priest and her Legion of
Mary group, had successfully stood up to him. The chief,
nonetheless, ensured that one of his young sons, Marcel, came
to live with my mother to protect her, or so he claimed. In
reality, Marcel was my uncle's eyes and ears, spying and
reporting on the goings-on in his late brother's house, which
he would have sold off were it not for Marité's vigilance.
Marcel rushed to inform his father of my return and my
intention to visit my father's tomb. At dawn, Marcel returned
and told my mother that my uncle strictly forbade me setting
foot in the village. I wanted to revolt against such an abuse of
power, but maternal wisdom, cutting short my recriminations,
reminded me: *He who knows the weight of the burden to be borne,
must have sufficient padding!*

I have always been impressed by my mother's collection of
proverbs. She had one for every situation in life. A few days
later, she convinced her elder brother to plead my case in front
of my uncle. When I tried to oppose this move, my mother's
response was *You must sweep your hut if you don't want scorpions in
it!* The chief organized a posthumous forgiveness ceremony,
and I was allowed to see my father's tomb. However, my inter-

actions with my uncle remained distant. This was not the only attempt to ostracize me though; in the neighbourhood, some idle cranks had attempted to forbid me entry to my mother's house. *We have to protect the old lady*, they yelled. *He's going kill her off, too.* My mother promptly chased them away. Today, some of them are regulars at La Goutte d'Or.

The first months of my return were tough. Even now, faced with a particularly malevolent look or those irresolvable equations that are part of the daily running of the shelter, I'm sometimes tempted to give in. I'm holding up, for now. No doubt because I don't have much time to think about myself. As director, mediator and, above all, confidante to disoriented youths, I come home each evening drained. 'I have gone from a laidback life of leisure to the toil of a labourer,' I complained to Elgep on the phone (which had certainly strengthened his conviction that it wouldn't be long before I came back to him). But time went on and I stayed. Two years have passed already since La Goutte d'Or opened, six months after my return. As soon as the first building was complete and the compound wall finished, I had a sign put up, soberly announcing: La Goutte d'Or – Youth Shelter. The first curious visitors stepped through the blue gate, and word of mouth did the rest. A few weeks after opening, the small reception was constantly full. While construction continued, I had several thatched pavilions built for various activities. Very quickly the busy hive started to resemble a compound of a hundred trades. You could find young people huddled around our first volunteers, learning to write a CV or motivation letter, while others tried out different trades on the available machines. Shortly, the many boys took over the place and the few girls who entered found them-selves sidelined. Natou, one of the mediators, advised me to build another pavilion specifically for girls. Under her guid-ance, they became emboldened, and some ventured to the car-pentry, electrical or even the car mechanic workshops, for which machinery had just arrived. The most sensitive matter to deal with was the arrival of young people who, like Jamal, had been rejected because of their sexual orientation. Some con-fided in me during the one-on-one interview I conducted with each new arrival. Had they heard rumours of my back-ground? They had been the initial target of my project, yet their arrival embarrassed me. Creating a specific group for them would have exposed them to stigmatization and condem-nation from the guardians of morality, ever on the lookout. I also understood that for some, their sexual orientation was ac-tually circumstantial. It was Jamal who brought this to my at-tention. I had firmly refused to let him return to the shelter, but he spent all his days there, harassing me like a gnat each time our paths crossed. 'You remember Rakiss?' he'd asked. I remembered the young Rakiss, barely twenty, as handsome and brazen as Jamal; we had lost trace of him for some time. Jamal went on to reveal that Rakiss had got it in his head to seduce Sebastien, the volunteer sent by the association in Avignon. 'Sebastien, who was not at all homo, confided in me.' In you? I'd cried, shocked. 'Don't get all worked up! Sebastien knew I was gay, maybe that's why! I talked to Rakiss, who is not one of *ours*. He confessed that he was trying his chances just like he had tried other ways to migrate.' That was that. Rakiss never came back to the shelter.

I was taken aback, both by the story itself and by the fact that it had happened right under my nose without me realising!

In some people's eyes, was La Goutte d'Or just a stepping stone while they waited for the great departure, just as one wears slippers while waiting to buy a pair of proper shoes? Leave! That was the only word they had on their lips. Many things may have changed in Ouabany, but that story remained immutable: for the deprived youth, salvation was elsewhere! They were filled with blinding anger, embittered against the whole world. Some of them hoped for the providential man who, like the Messiah, would finally lead them to the promised land of development. Others now only counted on the country being taken over by a dictator who would purge it of gangrenous corruption and gross mismanagement. For the most part, they just repeated slogans they picked up in the press or on social media. Nonetheless this sentiment was symptomatic of a state of mind that terrified me. 'What will you do with the opposition?' I questioned them, incredulous. 'Throw them in prison!' said one. 'No, we'd shoot them,' said another more radical youth. Just yesterday we were still fighting for our freedoms. What a step backwards! I was astounded, but I understood their rage. At home, the sensation was one of stagnation. On the world stage, the impression was that an open banquet was being held, available online but inaccessible in reality. These digitally connected youths, willing to skip meals to afford to use the internet, had front-row seats to watch a party they were excluded from attending. No sermon, no story of misadventure was able to convince the most determined of them not to try to sniff the aromas from closer quarters, to feel the contours of this gargantuan banquet. Matters were made worse by the lack of recreational facilities where this overflowing energy could be spent. In a country, a city and a neighbourhood filled with young people, not a single proper policy catered to their recreation. Did leaders not know that *when the people are entertained, they don't think of politics*?

The king of Denmark, Christian VIII, had had the ingenuity to construct the Tivoli Gardens to entertain his people holed up in the fortress that was Copenhagen. I organized a facility for my young interns for leisure activities after work. A long building that stood at the main entrance to La Goutte d'Or held offices and a huge multifunctional hall that served also as a canteen. The Resto, as we called it, turned into a games hall in the evenings, with a foosball table, a ping-pong table, board games and a corner bar under the stern watch of Igor, a mixed-race forty-year-old. When the USSR still existed, Igor's mother, charmed by the beautiful eyes of a Ouabany student in Kiev, had tried the African adventure. She became quickly disenchanted and left, abandoning her son. Poor Igor, also forsaken by his father who remarried a local, had to fend for himself very early on, taking on several jobs, including a stint as a hunting guide in the Zinga Reserve. After twenty-odd years in the bush, Igor returned to the city and ended up at La Goutte d'Or. Though stone-faced, he wasn't mean, but his imposing stature and sad look could intimidate. Igor, along with the watchman Mr Beogo and Maryse, who was in charge of the canteen, made up the permanent staff of the shelter.

Despite various difficulties, La Goutte d'Or built itself a reputation and we requested accreditation as a charitable organization. The fundraising campaigns that Elgep undertook were quite fruitful. I could have been content in my role as successful social entrepreneur. Why then did I have the taste of something unfinished on my tongue?

I confided my unease to Auntie Jeanne. In our moments of doubt, we each have our own therapies. Some go to see a psychologist; I went to see Auntie Jeanne. She is not my aunt, but I, too, used the affectionate term that everyone used to address her. Her political adversaries called her Calamity Jane, but only behind her back. Auntie Jeanne was a highly respected woman in Ouabany. Another of her nicknames was the Resistance, although she had never battled any war, if not one of ideas. The older people spoke of how she was a real revolutionary when she returned from Europe. Apparently after her law studies in Bordeaux, she had embarked on a backpacking tour of Europe. Few boys, much less girls, at that time would have dared to go on such an adventure. After traipsing away for ten years, to lands as far and mysterious as Lapland, she returned home with jarring ideas and attitudes. At first, no one was really suspicious of this forty-year-old with such a youthful face. With her cotton-print boubous and her angelic look, she must not have seemed in the least dangerous. And that's how people let down their guard. Before she arrived, no educated woman dressed in light boubous like the ones Auntie Jeanne favoured, for it was the crackling of rich Guinea brocade that announced the arrival of someone important. Whether man or woman, one did not finish university, even a local one, without broadcasting it to all and sundry. So, when this woman who had sat on the benches – or was it the armchairs? – of prestigious European universities, showed up in her boubous with colours more Hawaiian than African, people should've paid attention.

But you know people! They are stuck in their certitudes: *The president presides for life; men dominate women until the end of time!* A woman, even if educated, turning up with Hawaiian boubous and outlandish ideas about gender equality was nothing to get worked up about. And then, she created her party and ran for president twice, albeit unsuccessfully. *For the moment!* she would retort cheekily when her past came up. At almost seventy years of age, Auntie Jeanne was not ready to give up. At the last parliamentary elections, her party had won three seats. This ensured she had a platform, and she didn't miss any opportunity to use it. Currently, her main battle was youth emigration. Her questions to the government were followed, commented on and shared on social media by her young admirers. A few months after my return, I asked to meet her, also seduced by this impassioned personality. She received me in her law office, where she remained a lawyer alongside her political activity. When I told her about my project, she burst out laughing. You could write entire chapters describing Auntie Jeanne's inimitable laugh. It started out like a repressed cough, but that was just a false start. It then took off like a space rocket and, like a rocket, broke the sound barrier, inaudible for some seconds before it exploded as if it had misfired! What followed was a cascade of endless crashes. When you thought you'd heard the end, it restarted again, on and on to infinity. I waited patiently for it all to calm down. 'So, they funded you to come and convince young people not to leave?' she asked, before launching a new Ariane space rocket. When, finally, she had recovered a bit of her serenity, she explained her point of view. 'Young people here should also have the freedom to come and go. Why, at a moment when the world had never appeared more open, were they to be put under house arrest? I fight for the freedom of choice. They must be able to thrive, whether it be here or there! How can they contribute to the task of development if they're frustrated, angry? Leaders here are incompetent! They don't provide opportunities for training, for work!'

she thundered. 'And those in Europe think they can barricade themselves! What utopia!' And then, without any transition, she announced: 'We must organize a big march!' A march? I queried. 'Yes, a march, like Gandhi's for salt or Martin Luther King's march for civil rights! A march that leaves from the heart of Africa to go north, passing through the west!' She starting laying out a plan for the Freedom to Migrate March. 'A march for dignity!' I listened, enraptured. I loved the madness of Auntie *Cool*!

CHAPTER 13

The day hesitated to rise. There are mornings like that. The sun, with a premonition of the monstrosities it's going to illuminate, holds back its rays. A futile act of resistance. *God makes his sun rise over evil and good.* He makes it shine on good works and on abominations.

When I awoke, timid rays of light had penetrated the room. Despite the goat-like leaping of my vagabond mind, I was in an excellent mood. I had slept well, for the first time in a while. The past few weeks I'd regularly woken up between 3:00 a.m. and 3:15 a.m., the same terrifying dream repeatedly troubled my sleep. I am lying in a dark place, a bunker or a corridor, I can't tell. I can't use my limbs, nailed down or cut off, I can't tell. All around me are hundreds of rats waiting to pounce on me and devour me. Their eyes gleam dangerously in the dark. I can think of only one thing: How do I protect my eyes? I read somewhere that these creatures always start with 'the soft bits'! The circle of my assailants seemed to get closer with each nightmare. The largest huddled around my head. Perched on their rear hinds, they throw the reddened fire of their greedy eyes on the object of their desire. I could close my eyelids, but I would not be able to shut out the sinister beam. Aside from their teeth, which they seem to sharpen from time to time, the colony of rodents remains still, waiting for God knows what signal to launch the onslaught.

These unwelcome visits made my nights short, anguished and exhausting; but that morning, I awoke fresh and rested. No nightmare had cut short my sleep. I got out of bed and after some stretches, took a shower, and came out in high spirits and full of energy. I left the small house I occupied at the bottom of our large compound and headed toward the Resto. When I entered, the mediators, along with some early morning visitors and young people temporarily staying at the shelter, were sat on the benches set out along the tables, having breakfast. In a chorus, they wished me good morning, and I responded with a booming 'Hello, troops'. I was really in a good mood that morning of Friday 30 March. Maryse, who was at the counter, served me milk coffee in my large bowl, and I took a seat in the middle of the small group.

I loved this moment, the slow start to the day: silent communion while mouths were occupied by chewing and swallowing and therefore less available for discourse. The still crumpled faces would lighten up with each sip of coffee, tongues would loosen, and we'd ask each other's news before scattering off to our daily tasks.

My day's schedule was emptier than usual. I had to respond to a summons from the minister of cultural affairs, a sad-looking gnome with despotic manners. Having caught wind of our march, and not being able to summon Auntie Jeanne due to the separation of powers, the minister had summoned me. Intimidated by the ministerial summons, I contacted Auntie Jeanne, who had exploded in anger: 'Why is that midget sticking his nose into this? Is this a cultural march? We are marching for freedom, for the right to migrate!' I had difficulty convincing her not to show up unannounced at the minister's office. Protocol, separation of powers, Auntie Jeanne couldn't care less when her heart rose up. And her heart was well up on its feet recently due to all the pressure on us to give up our march.

It started with the two other MPs from her party. *It may not be the right time*, one of them had timidly objected when their party president presented the project. It was true that the state of affairs in the nation was troubled and deleterious. The ruling party had just imploded, undermined by infighting, and had split into two. One of the groups, composed of persons who, until then, were considered second fiddles, had rushed to proclaim its adherence to democratic values, thus rallying to it the progressive forces and throwing the other group into a dark abyss. At first glance, the split seemed to have cleared up the political scene. The opposition party, which had been rather arid until then, initially celebrated this new fertilization, but then was quickly disillusioned when they realized that they had just served as a stepping stone. Things were less Manichean than they appeared; they were much more complex. The Good were not necessarily on the side one expected, and Auntie Jeanne's miniscule party received solicitations from all sides. Constant in her convictions, Auntie desperately tried to preserve her independence, and that of her two fellow MPs. The latter, with their more fragile bases, were swaying like ficus in a storm. An intellectual terrorism draped in a cloak of righteousness took hold. Opportunists held their coats open, not knowing whether to wear them the right way or inside out. The bolder 'sure-of-themselvesers' had already put their horns to their lips to blow the tune of the day.

I have always admired people bound by certainties. I myself generally doubt, seek and, sometimes, acquire one or two convictions. I was now convinced that the march had to be organized despite the national imbroglio. Why was there so much agitation if it was just 'a loony initiative thought up by some scatterbrains', as the minister of foreign affairs had declared during a meeting with the diplomatic corps? The announcement of our movement had caused nervousness even beyond national borders. Several capitals involved, either as points of departure or destination for migrants or as passage and transit zones, alerted their ambassadors in Ouabany, who sought clarification. There was diplomatic commotion, political chaos and media cacophony. In the general confusion, it became fashionable to oppose the march and condemn its organizers. Auntie Jeanne and myself, identified as the original promoters of the seditious march, were thus caught in the middle of an international controversy within a national context of score-settling. The stream of marchers who joined our movement in ever-growing numbers at either La Goutte d'Or or on social media galvanized us. Before going to meet the honourable minister, I checked the March for Dignity website, and left for the ministry armed with one million likes and almost two hundred thousand registrations for the march.

The interview was more courteous than expected, but a sticky kind of courtesy that made me think that the ministers had divided roles between them: the stick for the minister of foreign affairs, and the carrot for the minister of cultural affairs. The *good* minister barely broached the subject of the march and focused instead on the activities of La Goutte d'Or, which he seemed to know rather well. He enquired about the state of our finances and dangled possible grants thanks a newly created

fund. As for our application to be accredited as a charitable organization, that was a mere formality. He would follow up on
this personally. Apparently, no one is incorruptible, you just
have to find the right price. That may be, but my life was precious to me, and I knew Auntie Jeanne would disembowel me
if I faltered. I offered my warmest smile to the minister and left
without saying anything.

As I arrived at La Goutte d'Or, I noticed an unusual crowd.
Were these new recruits? Why were they in front of the shelter
instead of inside? As I approached, I noticed their agitation.
People paced back and forth, glaring at each other and gesticu-
lating. Only anger could be behind such disorder! I skirted the
group, entered the compound, parked the car under the hangar
and stepped out to discover the cause of the commotion.
When I glimpsed Saul of Tarsus, my heart skipped a beat. I
thought we were rid of him. A few months ago, Saul of Tarsus
and his gang started spending their evenings at La Goutte d'Or.
Jamal, that dimwit, had introduced him to the shelter, and Saul
had brought with him a somewhat special crowd. They would
arrive around 7:00 p.m., tipsy, and take over the games hall,
forcing the other youths to be mere spectators.

When naming their child, some parents think only of their
own pleasure, of the sonorities that will ring nicely in their ears
when they or their loved ones pronounce the sweet name. If
there were no restrictions, we would have Hitlers, Stalins and
maybe even some Satans running freely around town! Yet a
name is an indelible mark on the forehead of each being, a
benediction or malediction for life. It influences the future of
its bearer. What an idea to call your son Saul of Tarsus! Saul of
Tarsus was a persecutor of Christians, a killer. Struck down and
blinded by divine force on the road to Damascus, he then

converted. He changed his name and became Paul, the greatest disciple of Christ after Peter. That the Bible contains other Saul of Tarsuses changed nothing in the matter. The name is tainted and drives one to diabolical acts.

Confronted with the intrusion of the undesired visitors, I had, in vain, tried to reason with Saul of Tarsus. At first, he pretended to act respectfully toward me. 'Elder brother,' he'd said, 'I promise that things will change. Hey guys, leave some space for the others!' he shouted to his band. But the next day, and the days after, nothing changed. When I broached the issue again, he laughed in my face and muttered: 'What does the *Auntie* want?' 'What? What did you say?' I had spluttered in anger. He didn't answer, but made obscene gestures with his friends before a round of high fives. Enraged, I had lost my cool and jumped at him, hitting him with an uppercut that threw him off balance. He would have fallen had his devotees not caught him. Regaining his spirits after a few seconds, he was charging at me with clenched fists, when Crankshaft stepped in.

Was it because of his bulging forehead that seemed to detach itself from the rest of his knobbly skull that someone had had the idea to nickname him Crankshaft? Did he protest the ridiculous moniker at the beginning? I have no idea. In any case, he'd adopted it as his own, and turned it into a pseudonym that he was, apparently, proud of.

'Crankshaft!' he introduced himself before accepting my outstretched hand as a sort of peace pipe to end the dispute that had pitted us against each other for several weeks. Crankshaft had a kiosk a few roads away from La Goutte d'Or. His wife, like most of our neighbours, came to draw water from the shelter's borehole when the national water supply failed.

She was a young, pretty woman. One of the youths at the shelter had the bad idea to tease her about her husband's ugliness. She had told her husband, and he had arrived at the shelter, furious, demanding the skin of the rude idiot. We refused to reveal who had made the comment. The stand-off lasted some time, and then one day I stopped at his kiosk, ordered a coffee and suggested that we make peace. His head may have been knobbly, but Crankshaft's spirit was as smooth and pure as his adorable young daughter, Jasmine's.

On more than one occasion since our handshake I had witnessed how big a heart he had. The day of my altercation with Saul of Tarsus, Crankshaft had succeeded in getting the gang to leave without any violence and then alerted the Zoebambas, a neighbourhood vigilante group. While they were strongly criticized by legal experts, the Zoebambas were tolerated by the residents of neighbourhoods on the outskirts, deserted by security forces. They showed up at La Goutte d'Or, and from then on, we had to pay them a monthly tax for our protection. Calm returned and I never heard from Saul of Tarsus again.

And now here Saul of Tarsus was again in broad daylight, in the middle of an angry crowd including individuals with barely concealed bludgeons, steel bars and other assorted instruments of death. When he saw me coming, Saul of Tarsus rushed toward me shouting: 'You give him to us or we will burn your shelter!' I ignored him and addressed Maryse, 'What is he talking about?' Maryse took me inside the shelter and explained that Jamal, chased by Saul of Tarsus's gang, had taken refuge at La Goutte d'Or.

'Why are they chasing him?'

'They claim that Jamal stole a mobile phone the gang leader had just given to his younger brother. Jamal doesn't deny taking the phone, but claims he was just taking back the money that Saul of Tarsus had borrowed from him.'

'Where is he?'

'In your lodgings,' responded Maryse.

'You gave him the keys?'

'They'd invaded the Resto, Igor and Crankshaft had trouble getting them out,' she explained a bit sheepishly.

I went back out to handle the sensitive situation and, if need be, alert the head of the Zoebambas. He was already there, with the members of his militia, doubling the size of the crowd I had found on my arrival fifteen minutes earlier. He was talking to Saul of Tarsus at some distance from the crowd. When I approached them, it was he who addressed me first: 'Bring out the *homophile!*'

'What?' I stuttered, shocked.

'The paedophile!' corrected Saul of Tarsus, a diabolical smile on his lips.

What story had he invented to get the head of the Zoebambas on his side? The others moved in and formed a circle around us. I felt oppressed. I had the unfortunate intuition that this was no longer an issue to do with Jamal, stolen phone or of a debt to reimburse.

'He's a paedophile!' someone behind me repeated.

Who was he talking about? The word run through the crowd, eliciting enquiry; many didn't know its meaning.

'A rapist of children!' explained the same strong voice. This time, everyone understood.

The ranks closed around me without any form of trial. The first blow hit me on the temple. In a fraction of a second, I understood what was happening. I struggled against them, tried to explain the mix-up, but I knew it was a lost cause. The last image that I made out was Crankshaft's stupefied face as he tried to cut through the crowd shouting something that I already couldn't hear. Poor Crankshaft! I thought.

EPILOGUE

The Wambtaba market took place every Friday at the western exit of the village, on a site with a peculiar history. An enormous anthill stood in the middle of the weekly marketplace. The elders claimed it had been there since the time of their fathers, their fathers' fathers, and even earlier. That is to say, the anthill had been there before the village was founded. In any event, it was there that newborn twins used to be buried alive, out of superstition. The poor beings, feared by residents who saw them as malevolent djinns, were put to death as soon as they had been expelled, along with their placentas. Nothing that was reminiscent of those evil creatures was to remain. The poor, powerless mothers could do nothing but swallow their pain, dry their tears and pray for the benediction of the ancestors so that the next pregnancy wouldn't be a multiple one. This barbaric custom was now nothing more than a distant painful memory, but the village chief, again out of superstition, had opposed opening up a market in the accursed place, and so a site toward the east had been chosen. But sellers of unusual meats — dog, donkey, horse — withdrew to the cursed site, bringing with them their clients and then women selling local brew. From then, the eastern site lost all chance and, against the will of the chief, the souls of sacrificed twins drew this weekly gathering. The Wambtaba market quickly became a curiosity. Lovers of rare meats from the nearby city came to get their fix at the market, and tourists, drawn by the incredible story of the martyred babies, also visited.

That Friday, the market had just started buzzing with activity when the sky suddenly darkened. Butchers rushed to hastily wrap up their carcasses and skewered meat brochettes, and the local brew-sellers protected their enormous jars with plastic covers. Everyone rushed to protect themselves from the first drops of this unexpected rain. That was when it perched on the top of the anthill. It took in the agitation with its globular eyes. Those who had noticed it were seized with unease and alerted others around them. Whispering, as if the ominous bird could understand them, some linked its arrival to the disappearance of the vultures. For some weeks now, the sinister birds had vanished into thin air. In other places such a departure would be reason for joy, but here, where they played the role of garbage collectors, their presence was a sign of the affluence and vigorous health of the village and its inhabitants. Vultures disappearing was never a sign of good things. That in itself had already been cause for alarm. The unmoving presence of this bird of prey, on market day, was a confirmation of imminent disaster.

Someone had the presence of mind to alert the chief. After a quick consultation with his advisors, the chief ordered that the competent persons proceed with ritual sacrifices. While children chased after chickens, whose blood was needed for the libation to cast the spell, Marcel arrived with the news.

The United Nations building, located in the centre of Ouabany, is one of the tallest in the city. From her office on the fifth floor, Marité had a commanding view. It was her lunch break and she was in front of her window, stretching her legs. Her phone rang. It was Maryse, her voice broken by sobs: 'Come quick, something bad has happened, something really bad!'

Old El Hajj, called upon by Marité, summoned the other elders in the neighbourhood to deliberate. How would the horrible news be announced to Simone? Two elderly mamas were sent out as harbingers. When they arrived in front of Simone's gate, they were met with a scream that turned their blood to ice. They entered as Simone, sitting under the shade of a mango tree, threw the transistor radio that she always carried. Hysterically, she screamed, 'Liars! It's not true, it's not true!'

Marité, who followed close behind the harbingers, entered in a rush. She was just in time to catch her mother – who realized upon seeing Marité that the news she'd heard on the radio was indeed real – as she collapsed.

Elgep, on his part, didn't scream. Perhaps he collapsed after having listened to what Marité had to say. No one was there to witness. He was all alone, under his new gazebo, enjoying the spring afternoon. When the phone rang, he thought of Jeanphi, who the day before had finally agreed to spend a month-long holiday in Apt before the March for Dignity in September. Marité had spoken with great tact, but he knew how devastated she herself must have been. He calmly asked some questions, wanting all the details of the macabre scene his sister-in-law had found in front of the shelter. 'Did you take photos?' he asked. Marité explained that when she arrived at the tragic scene, all onlookers had left. There were only policemen and the ambulance team working, observed at a distance by the staff and some of the youths from La Goutte d'Or, all in tears. She ended her account by exhorting him to be brave. He, in turn, offered her some words of consolation, said he would arrive the next day, and hung up.

Translation copyright © Yarri Kamara 2022

Originally published as *Si loin de ma vie* by Le Serpent à Plumes, 2018.

tiltedaxispress.com

The rights of Monique Ilboudo to be identified as the author and Yarri Kamara as the translator of this work have been asserted in accordance with Section 77 of the Copyright, Designs and Patent Act 1988.

ISBN (paperback) 9781911284802

ISBN (ebook) 9781911284796

A catalogue record for this book is available from the British Library.

Cover art: Soraya Gilanni Viljoen

Cover design, author and translator illustration: Haricha Abdaal

Edited by: Alyea Canada, Saba Ahmed, and Joely Day

Proofreader: Mayada Ibrahim

Typesetting and ebook production: Abbas Jaffary

Publisher: Kristen Vida Alfaro

Community Manager: Tice Cin

Managing Editor: Theodora Danek

Foreign Rights Director: Julia Sanches

Publicity: Hana Sandhu

Made with Hederis

Printed and bound by Clays Ltd, Elcograf S.p.A.

ABOUT TILTED AXIS PRESS

Tilted Axis is a non-profit press publishing mainly work by Asian writers, translated into a variety of Englishes. This is an artistic project, for the benefit of readers who would not otherwise have access to the work – including ourselves. We publish what we find personally compelling.

Founded in 2015, we are based in the UK, a state whose former and current imperialism severely impacts writers in the majority world. This position, and those of our individual members, informs our practice, which is also an ongoing exploration into alternatives – to the hierarchisation of certain languages and forms, including forms of translation; to the monoculture of globalisation; to cultural, narrative, and visual stereotypes; to the commercialisation and celebrification of literature and literary translation.

We value the work of translation and translators through fair, transparent pay, public acknowledgement, and respectful communication. We are dedicated to improving access to the industry, through translator mentorships, paid publishing internships, open calls and guest curation.

Our publishing is a work in progress – we are always open to feedback, including constructive criticism, and suggestions for collaborations. We are particularly keen to connect with Black and indigenous translators of Asian languages.

tiltedaxispress.com
@TiltedAxisPress